The Princess & the Pink N

by

Janine Regan-Sinclair

A 21st Century Journey to Enlightenment

The Angel Warrior Series

The Angel, the Witch & the Warrior - Book 1

Saving the World from my Bathtub - Book 2

The Princess & the Pink Moon Leeches – Book 3

The Avatar & the Crystal Key – Book 4

Published in the United Kingdom
by
Crystal Ki Press

Printed and bound in Great Britain by
CPI Antony Rowe, Chippenham and Eastbourne

ISBN: 978-0-9559745-2-6

It is currently the law that authors and publishers must publish a disclaimer regarding the advice given in books relating to complementary therapies. As a complementary practitioner I am not allowed to make any claims as to the effectiveness of exercises or treatments referred to in this book.

Therefore any information and exercises given are intended as a guide only. Neither the author nor publisher can accept any responsibility for any effects resulting from any exercises or treatment included in this book.

Although this book is mainly fictional, it does refer to some factual complementary therapies and treatments. The information in this book is not a substitute for professional health care and readers are advised see a medical practitioner in the case of illness.

Please note that I have used the word negative in this book in regard to certain energies. It is a general word to describe low frequency energy, disharmony, dark energy, false information, impurities and imbalance. There is no such thing as negative energy as it all comes from God. The whole point is to remove the imbalance and fill the gaps with balance and one word describes all.

Contents

Dedicated with love..................

This book is dedicated to all of my friends, especially Trish; she has been a rock and a ray of sunshine throughout the writing of them and my journey so far. Thank you, much love x x x

The Angel Warrior series of books

Introduction

There are now 7 books in the Angel Warrior series. These books have been based on factual astral journeys and personal healing sessions I have experienced. My goal is to educate and help people attain higher levels of consciousness and to raise their vibration through self healing and purification. The series of books explain what you can expect to happen during your out of body attunements and initiations by higher beings, as you develop spiritually. Many people are not aware that their consciousness and their vibration are two completely different things. Your consciousness refers to your mind, and your vibration relates to the purity of your entire being, mind and body, especially your body. You must treat all areas in order to progress; simply becoming a space cadet (head in the astral planes) is not enough for you to ascend fully. They are also simply an amazing diary of events forming the story of the life of a spiritual warrior and a single mum known as Janine of Warwick in the spiritual planes.

The next book is The Avatar & the Crystal Key is the 4th in the series. All of my books follow on from factual information given in the 1st book; which if you work with the exercises using the grids and nets, can take you to Master level attainment in your ascension process. It is important to read them in order if you want to follow the path described in them. The techniques taught in my workshops and described in my 1st book can take you from Enlightened Master, into Saint Level and beyond Avatar Supreme, with some dedication and self purification. You do need to work on a regular basis to achieve the higher levels of attainment. No one became an Enlightened Master sitting watching TV; it takes work and it is a life style, that means your diet will also need to become purer, no wheat, dairy or sugars for a start: don't panic, you can give them up a bit at a time. You will also need to remove the seed fear of enlightenment. The good news is, we can do it and still work and have a family. We do not need to lock ourselves away in monasteries or retreats anymore.

Book 2 took you to Planetary Prince/Princess vibration and this book will take you through the next part of my journey, and hopefully you may want to follow a similar path. It will give you an insight into what you can expect as you work your way towards Saint level vibration. Like book 2, it is also a good read as a story book for those with a short attention span.

In order to follow the attainment figures, you need to know a bit about the original map of consciousness and how creation works. All of this is explained in my 2nd book Saving the World from my Bathtub and I advise you again to read the books in the correct order they were released. That way, one can follow the Crystal Ki map of consciousness figures and absorb the information given in them.

The Map of Consciousness was created by a spiritual teacher called Dr David Hawkins in order to calibrate where we are on the spiritual path in relation to consciousness, the journey back to Source, and total self realisation. Crystal Ki works on a similar scale but from 0 – 10,000+ rather than 0 – 1000. The Crystal Ki map of consciousness also refers to vibration and not just the mind.

1. The Crystal Ki Map of Consciousness

The Crystal Ki Map of consciousness follows on from Dr David Hawkins map of consciousness and gives you an indication of where you are in your ascension process allowing those of you who have been to a Crystal KI workshop to follow your path knowing what level you are at now and your next major attainment level. If you astral travel, you can be consciously aware of all of your out of body attunements and initiations in the spiritual realms.

The figures refer to both consciousness and vibration because in order to reach the higher levels on the map you need to work on clearing your mind and body: that means regular healing, exercise and a first class diet that eliminates alcohol, wheat, sugar and dairy products over a period on time. You will be guided by your higher mind as you develop.

The map helps you to keep track of where you are and what level you calibrate. These figures show you that you vibrate at the same frequency as a Saint or an Ascended Master, not that you instantly become one. It is important to keep the ego under control, there is no need to be running around telling the world you are an Avatar, real Avatars would not feel the need to do that, in fact keeping silent about their level of power would be a part of the spiritual contract they will have agreed to. Only the ego self would want to let the world know that they are more important than anyone else.

That being said, let's have a look at the map, it will give you an idea of the attainment possibilities we have even though we are in a human body...........

Calibration	Spiritual Attainment Level
0 - 200	Lower Levels of Consciousness,
	greed, apathy, guilt, fear, blame, etc
200	Integrity (Book 1)
400	Wisdom
500	Heart Open
600	Higher Heart Open
700	First level of Enlightenment (Book2)
950	Master (E = Essence)
1050	Enlightened Master (E)
1500	Ascended Master (E)
1750	Planetary Prince / Princess (E) (Book3)
2000	Emperor/Empress (E - Local Universe)
3000	God / Goddess (E - Local Universe)
3500	Saint
4000	Avatar (Book 4)
5000	Avatar Supreme
6000	Rishi (Surrender Free Will) (Book 5)
7000	Angel
8000	Archangel
9000	Galactic Master (Book 6)
10,000	Oversoul
11,000+	Time Lord (Book 7)

2. 4th Sept 2008 - Day 1 Planetary Princess

Yesterday I humbly accepted my new position as Planetary Princess. A major achievement, one might say, but to be honest I still feel quite normal; and in general, down to earth even though I spend about one hour a day out of body, travelling through the other realms and the local universe. Working with

11

ascended and galactic masters seems like normal behaviour to me but if people knew what I can do, they would freak and I would be waiting for a knock at the door from the men in white coats, keen to cart me off to the local loony bin.

I was talking to a close friend of mine the other day about my latest book. She asked me what it was about and this is what I told her.....It's about an enlightened healer, (a light worker) who astral travels; and having read a book called 'Universal Soul' by Chris Thomas (which blames a lot of planet Earth's problems on outside influences, namely by ET life forms) decides to take matters into her own hands; and working with the Archangel Michael, she gathers the ETs up amongst other off world looters and deports them.

In the process she learns many secrets of the laws of creation and comes across all sorts of alien beings, demons, entities and general negative energy forms. Using special nets made of diamond light energy, she removes them with the help of angelic beings and God. Her goal is to aid in the ascension of the planet by cleaning up Mother Earth and her aura and filling the gaps with lighter, purer energy.

It's all done while she lies meditating in her bath tub, hence the title of book 2 "Saving the World from my Bath Tub". While working as a therapist, she develops new ways to move energy using her mind aided by her spirit guides. During the sessions, she removes her old issues from her energetic bodies and raised her own frequency and consciousness in an amazing soul journey, where she attains through Master to Enlightened Master and even further to the level of 1750 on the new map of consciousness, which is Planetary Princess. In short, she accepts spiritual responsibility for Urantia (Earth) and signs a spiritual contract to keep it clean, jokingly referring to herself as Gods cleaning lady.

It's all done without fuss and with the help of a few other light workers and friends, who are also awake. Their secret meetings help to cleanse Mother Earth and subdue the consequences of fear based behaviour, created by the dark side, which currently control the most powerful positions on the planet. That's about it really.

My friend just looks at me and says "Wow, it sounds exciting!"

"Yep, it can be", I thought. If she only knew it was all true. It was me who was the Princess and the immense power God has trusted me with; she would pass out; after calling for the man in white coats of course!

I woke up this morning and placed my orb of protective light (camouflaged) beneath my feet, closed my chakras and asked my higher self to place the protection around me, needed for that day. A quiet prayer and I was up and about.

Day 1 as Planetary Princess; what does God have in store for me today? I decided to just take a normal bath and not to leave my body. I deserved a day off now and then. As I lay in the warm water, my mind wandered. I recall an email sent last year by Helena, a lovely woman I had met through my work, who became a student. She wrote to me asking if there was a willow tree in the bottom left of my garden (she had never been to my home). She said that the willow tree was going to help me with my work. How right she was. Willow often helps me figure out ways of clearing energies and he also guides me when I need some wise words; he's quite a character. He slapped me across the face last year for smoking a cigarette after my nephew's funeral. I had given up a couple of years before and it was a temporary lapse; I haven't touched one since. I now realised how wise the trees are and Willow is a wise and trusted friend. Luckily for me she was awake, and when I told her about my conversation with Willow, she was pleased that I didn't think she was mad by sending me the email. I never think anyone is mad; I always have an open mind. I lay there feeling quite content with my status and began to fall asleep. Next thing I knew, I was lying in a cold bath and wrinkled like a prune.

The day was like most days, nothing weird or strange or did I speak to soon. I had an overwhelming urge to go and lie down on my bed; it was 5pm, a bit late for an afternoon nap. As soon as I lay down, I said the words "May God's will be done" and closed my eyes. I could see the universe spread out before me in all of its glory, and a line of golden light about an inch thick began to come out of my chest, my heart in fact. The line went out and around in a circle and back through my heart; and then again and again forming circles of light, hoops of golden energy forming a huge ball, like a ball of string without a centre; a hollow ball of string.

It formed a shell of light and at the centre a spark. I remember thinking that it was a seed atom, the divine spark. The seed of light grew and grew until the hollow was no more. The ball of light formed a crust, like the surface of the moon, a pink moon full of golden light. The edge was attached to my chest, it was the size of a football pitch compared to me; then the chord was cut, so to speak, and it broke free from my heart and drifted off into the darkness to join the other planets and stars. "Good grief! I've just given birth to a planet, albeit from my heart. What the ...!" And that was that, another normal day in the life of

Janine of Warwick. Time for dinner, there were dishes in the sink, a woman's work is never done.

3. 5th Sept 2008 – No Healing Centre

One of my clients rang me earlier to tell me that her continuous struggle with aliens had been brought to an abrupt halt by breaking 46 contracts she had made prior to her incarnation. We will all have some sort of contract to fulfil but they are not always for our highest good, and it is important to cancel them if they are harming us. After I finished the call I realised that I needed to speak to the Karmic Board as it was a message telling me that my spiritual contracts were about to change.

Early 2008, four colleagues and I tried to manifest a healing clinic in the centre of town. Since then the once group of five had now become two, as we moved in other directions. For the last eight months I had been working towards opening a new holistic clinic, a spiritual place of learning dedicated to helping people with cancer, mainly. My dream was about to be shattered, but it wasn't a shock. I was prepared for the worst as I made my way to the retreat and spoke to the Divine Director. I was informed that spirit had decided that I was to let the centre go and would be guided to another one. Okay, fine, I thought; then I began to feel really upset about it all. I find change quite stressful, and after the meeting I was very emotional, and cried on and off for the next two days.

This was causing a block in my heart to clear, another disappointment. It really knocked me back. I felt lost and unsure of my future, I felt completely out of control of my life and it was scary. I was an enlightened soul, but I still had old rubbish in my system from past lives that needed clearing.

4. 7th Sept 2008 – The Hadron Collider

I spoke to Jo today. She was telling me about a machine developed in Switzerland called the Large Hadron Collider. It was a 17 mile coil of magnets in a tunnel, somewhere in Switzerland, a huge physics experiment using a magnetic field to crash atoms into one another in order to try and find out where they end up, because they disappeared after the collision completely, as if by magic.

She said she was worried about it and thought that I needed to look into it. So, I called my friend John and we set up a meeting the night before the big bang that was planned. We would get together on Tuesday at my place and do what we could. The experiment was due to take place on Wednesday lunch time, with massive media coverage.

I had heard about this machine about four years ago; a friend had read about it and I remember at the time thinking that the dark side could be involved, somehow. If you had a machine that could move energy to other dimensions and you were, shall we say, less than light, what would you do with it? My suspicions were one of two possibilities. To collect the energy and use Earth as a giant battery to use it as a weapon of some sort, like a ray gun, but with James Bond style consequences. I've always had a good imagination but I was about to find out the truth in a couple of days time.

5. 8th Sept 2008 – The Pink Moon Leeches

I have been feeling under the weather for some weeks now; I had a rash on my arms that turned out to be a fungal infection. I was tired all of the time and drained mentally. I connected to my individual bodies during a meditation and asked my physical body, my mental body, my emotional body and my spiritual body, what they all needed from me and they were not in a good way. My mental body had two huge bumps on the head from worrying about things too much. My emotional body really needed some love and support and Steven was working away, so no chance of that for a few weeks. My spiritual body was OK but needed to retreat for a while.

Mostly I was drained by this skin infection and mentally, albeit on a sub conscious level. I was worried about my sister who had cancer, and my mum, whose kidneys were failing. It was also the first anniversary of the murder of my nephew; no wonder I was a bit low.

I asked my higher self what was in my new contract and was informed that it was still being written. When I enquired about the Large Hadron Collider, I was told that we would know what to do on Tuesday and not to worry.

I had no idea why, but there seemed to be an environmental epidemic of parasites at the moment and they were contaminating my chakras every chance they had. So I decided I needed to call in the help of the Pink Moon Leeches. An Angel told me about them, she handed them to me in a crystal box. These little leeches were clear like diamonds with tiny pink hearts and they were from the future, apparently they evolved on the planet I gave birth to; fascinating! The Angel opened the box and poured the little creatures carefully into my stomach. They swam around inside me and in no time at all, they had absorbed the sticky black residue the parasites had created. As the little helpers floated up, they were dark with the rubbish they had absorbed but as soon as they returned to their crystal box they were pure and clear once more. The magic box had purified the darkness, I blew a kiss to them; it turned into lots and lots of tiny pink butterflies, which then entered their little hearts, one each - a thank you gift.

6. 9th Sept 2008 – The Laser Gun

The large Hadron Collider was to be unveiled on the world tomorrow and something was amiss. Jon came over to my place and after a brief chat about what was going on, how the machine worked and my concerns related to previous information I had been given. We settled down in my lounge and began our journey. We were told that we should shape shift before we went astral, and were to take care. Archangel Michael called us the SAS, Secret Angel Service, which we found highly amusing even though, in a way, it was apt.

The machine was underground in a tunnel and once we were tuned in Jon could see the tunnel and what he described as a type of laser gun. His voice grew concerned as he looked further. It was being pulled by two set of beings. The correct course was 12 o 'clock but there were a group of dark beings trying to pull the line of fire towards 2 o'clock, (headed for a planet in our local universe). This would have had a catastrophic effect on our planet, and the other inhabited planets, if it was targeted as per their intention. Towards 10 o'clock he could see a group of light workers doing their best to pull the machine back to where it should be. John said that the darker beings were of low intelligence and seemed to be under the control of someone more sinister. They were sitting with their hands over the top of their heads as if that would stop them being seen; like small children placing their hands over their faces and convinced you can't see them.

As John was on the ground informing me of what was happening, I felt I was at a higher altitude. I could see the whole area as if I was a mile or so above the scene. Then my heart stopped beating. I had a Demon staring me right in the eye, he was about 3 ft away; I was silent and stealth but he could sense me, I knew it. His yellow eyes with vertical slit pupils stared at me threateningly and I acted with a speed I had never known before; he was in a net. Archangel Michael held him out in front of him like a bag of shopping, angry, writhing and cursing. This startled the group. I netted 90% but they scattered here, there, all over the area. I called to my band of light.

"Help, get them", and the Angels were like white rangers; they caught each and every one of the perpetrators with their trusty butterfly nets.

"Did you see that Demon John," "Yes he's not happy," he replied.

The beast with the yellow eyes reminded me of the old drawings of the Devil with the features of a ram, horns and hooves; like you see on old tarot cards.

"Peace be with you", I repeated as he struggled in the net bag and he calmed down; exhausted and stripped of his army he sat like a scorned child in the bottom of the net, and in came a huge hand from the heavens and whipped him off. It was Abba, I was so relieved.

We had done the important work, a little clearing here and there and then we performed a brief verbal ceremony, ensuring the machine could not be used in a way that could cause harm. We ended with a prayer for the protection of the scientists from evil, in the hope that this machine would be used only to benefit mankind in the future. Our mission complete, we were home, what a buzz!

7. 11th Sept 2008 – The White Garden

I dealt myself a few oracle cards this morning and I had the trickster, which was always a warning to be on my guard when I was astral, and the sun, showing a beautiful walled garden with two children playing in it. Later, as I lay in my salt bath cleansing my aura, I was guided to go and see Willow. I crossed over a beautiful bridge and sat inside his trunk; it was like a big cushioned arm chair and Willow was in good spirits. We had a quick chat and he told me to go with Andrew, my underwater guide who sat waiting for me, next to the pond in my garden.

As I greeted Andrew, something felt odd. I sensed his essence was a low vibration and when he placed his arms around me I knew exactly who it was... Satan. I threw a net around him and he was gone. Moments later the real Andrew arrived, we both then turned into frogs, jumped into the pond and headed for Atlantis. As I entered the crystal city, Andrew waited by the gates. I walked up a crystal staircase to a large coffin size casket and opened the lid. It was dull, not the bright healing light I expected, and so I called for Abba. Satan (the trickster) was on his toes today, it was the third attempt before the real Abba emerged. I was getting tired of Satan's games, but there was nothing I could do. Abba filled the casket with liquid crystals, shimmering, opalescent diamonds, beautiful was an understatement. As he stood outside, I entered the liquid and lay outside the casket to let the crystals do their stuff. Once I had absorbed this glorious energy, I climbed out and I could see sunflowers everywhere, stunning like sky scrapers in the sunshine. We walked over to meet Andrew and Abba told him that we were going to the garden and Andrew swam off in the direction we had come from. Abba and I walked along the ocean bed towards a cave. We entered the cave which was filled with bright

20

light. There was lots of tube like passage ways into the rocks. It was an intricate portal, I couldn't help but feel that I had been here before, and then I remembered. This was the cradle of life. Abba suddenly entered one of the light ways and I found myself staring at his feet, as we travelled at speed through the beautiful tunnel. Within minutes we were outside and in what looked like Peru. We then entered a lift shaft in the wall. As the lift ascended the walls and floor became transparent, we went higher and higher, through the clouds, out of the Earth's atmosphere, until the planet just looked like a small ball thousands of miles below us. We came to a step and the doors slid open; white clouds and white light. I was sure that we were in Heaven but I had to ask,

"Abba, are we in Heaven?" I asked.

"Yes, my child." He replied.

"Am I dead?"

He laughed and said, "No, my child. I have brought you here for a brief rest. You need the peace it can give you. You have worked very hard and are in need of recuperation. Come, let us rest a while."

As we walked through the clouds, they began to disappear and we entered the most beautiful garden I had ever seen or imagined possible. We sat down on a silky white bench. All sorts of animals began to appear and walked towards us without fear or hesitation. They wanted to be touched by us; there were dears, rabbits, birds, butterflies, all in a row, just like a scene from Snow White. It really was heaven. As I looked over my shoulder I could see two giraffes standing behind us.

"Giraffes are my favourite, such loving creatures." said Abba.

"I didn't think God had favourites." I replied.

"I do love the Giraffes" he smiled.

As we sat and chatted about my future, he told me I should not worry so much and have faith. He wasn't giving too much away though. I was being kept in the dark about something but I felt it was for the best; too much information can cause problems. He told me that Sananda loved this garden and came here often to be at peace and that now I knew how to get here, I could visit whenever I wanted. I could use it as a place of retreat and to talk to the animals, how wonderful, I am so lucky.

We stayed and talked like old friends and after about half an hour we made our way back to the lift, and it brought me down to Earth, and into my own little secret garden. I stepped out and Abba was gone. I said thank you to everyone, and I was home.

8. 13th Sept 2008 – A Broken Third Eye (1786)

Yesterday I was clearing my chakras when I pulled out what looked like a huge piece of broccoli. I was unaware at the time, but it quickly dawned on me that it was symbolic of fungi. I had a fungal skin infection (so the doctor told me) which I was treating with flower formulas. I set my intention to clear the infection, and the live fungal energy from my body, and pulled out six or seven nets with broccoli type energy in them. I felt much better afterwards. My calibration had gone up as a result to 1786.

I spoke to someone at the bank today over the telephone, and I had such a headache afterwards. It was my own fault; I had forgotten to close my chakras. Whatever was attached to the woman I had spoken to, had stuck what looked like a pencil in my head, my third eye to be precise; I needed to clear it. I settled into my tub and used the nets to remove toxins and other pollutants from my body. I then asked an angel to pull the pencil out of my forehead. The pain went instantly, but the crystal in my chakra was broken, so I waited while the angel swept the broken fragments into a bag and asked Abba for a new crystal. I could see it floating towards me, but having been caught out in the past by just placing objects given to me straight into my chakras, and realising that all that glistens is not gold, I decided to check it was fine and drop it into a Crystal Ki net. If it fell through the net it was pure, if it stayed in the net, it was fake. This particular crystal, which looked like a 2 inch diameter diamond, fell through the net and was caught in my left hand and promptly placed in my brow; I could see again.

I walked across to Willow and he pointed toward Andrew; next thing I knew, we were swimming to the crystal city and the healing casket. Andrew always waited at the entrance as I lay in the pure light coffin shaped box. Layers and layers of discs of neon blue and white light passed through me one after another, from head to toe. I felt fantastic when I climbed out and swam with Andrew for a while, just for fun.

When we got back to the garden my old friend White Bear was waiting on his stunning magical carpet and he beckoned me to jump on board. We made our way to Mt Shasta and rested on the mountain top. The Mountain told me that Emma was potentially a Crystal Ki Master, there would only be seven in total

23

apart from me, and I was thrilled not only for me but for her as well - this news would make her day.

Later today for some reason I felt the need to have another bath and was guided to go and see the Divine Director. He wanted me to clear some ET's and other life forms that had poured through at epidemic levels, and were causing chaos throughout the local universe. No problem, I had soon collected nearly 43,000 of those beings; little lost souls and the Angels took them to Abba as was the done thing when dealing with other life forms. This put my new level up to 1812, I had hit Planetary Princess and my crown was encrusted with a huge diamond, the size of a postage stamp or near enough.

As I made my way back with Archangel Michael, I was silent; I was thinking about the new map of consciousness and how the original one only went up to 1000. The new one went up as far as 10,000 with the following initiations by the White Brotherhood as one attained.

CALIBRATION LEVEL	% of KARMA CLEARED	No. OF SOULS ENLIGHTENED
1500	51%	250,000
	Ascended Master level	
1750	58%	500,000
	Planetary Prince/Princess	
1850	65%	600,000
	PP Level 2	
1950	75%	750,000
	PP Level 3	
2000	100%	1,000,000
	Emperor of local universe	

These initiations could not be given by man. One had to earn them through self purification and dedication to service of not only mankind, but by universal

24

service to all life forms, without judgement, and with love and compassion. The tests were tough too. I had a feeling that when I attained 2000, Sananda would pass this local universe to me to take care of and he would move on. Either that or my imagination was running wild again. The men in white coats flashed through my mind. I knew I wasn't crazy because every now and then I questioned my sanity and only sane people do that, mad people never question their sanity.

9. 14th Sept 2008 – Eggs and Chips

I had a workshop today, three ladies all grown up (over 40) and we cleared some interesting energy. One of the girls asked me where the eggs were coming from, she was finding in her aura. This was the bit in the workshop when I get to tell them about how the ET's lay eggs in our auras – crazy but true. I was pleasantly surprised at how easily they absorbed and accepted this information. I explained about the large crusty eggs that surrounded the aura and how to remove them by simply asking Archangel Michael to cut the egg in half and visualise it being done. Your emails can't reach you if you have an egg around your aura, it's always a sign for me.

Once we were onto the subject of aliens, I told the group about extra terrestrial chips I had read about in 'Universal Soul' by Chris Thomas, and how once I had been made aware of them, I began to find them on a regular basis in some of my clients, students and even myself. The girls were wide eyed at this point, the information was shocking but they were hungry for more. I told them about how some of these things had been placed in our energetic bodies before we incarnated and allowed us to be used as batteries, an energy supply and as a remote viewing tool. The chips look like small flying saucers, some looked like spinning wheels and others were more intricate with plugs wires and discs. The girls were amazed, these things are every day to me but it must be an eye opener to the new light workers. They all embraced the information and when we got down to the practical part of the workshop, one of them actually had a disc shaped chip in her heart which they could all see and feel; it was a perfect example.

As they all had a turn at being the patient, we would use the grids and our hands to feel the different energy blocks and the relevant sensations. Kate lay on the couch and I had a quick feel of her aura about 3 inches away from her body. It felt cool and seemed to be covering her whole left side. I moved over to the right, and it felt the same. I quickly realised that I could feel her layer of protection, she was wearing a suit of armour made of light. This was great. I said nothing and asked the other two girls to see what they could feel. Immediately one of them said that she could sense shiny metal and that it seemed to be covering her whole body.

I smiled and looked at Kate and said "Brilliant; now Kate would you mind removing your suit of armour, so we can work on you."

She was really pleased because this proved to her that she was doing it right. She had put the protection around her just as I had taught her and it worked as we could all feel it. The girls were impressed and confidence levels increased. The workshop was a real success. Eggs and chips!

10. 15th Sept 2008 – The Stars in my Chakras

As I lay in the bath, my mind was elsewhere. What did the future hold for me? If I am on the right path, and I believe I am, why am I broke? I loathed taking money for healing work I carried out. I had some kind of block regarding money and I needed to sort it out before I was bankrupt. I pulled a net or two through me as I always did and I became engulfed in a tube of light, it was clear light, see through, but definitely a tube. It felt good, so I just went with it. A star appeared above me and as it moved down through my chakras it left a star (a replica of itself) in each one of them. They were like prisms radiating light that I could touch, it felt so pure. I could have been lifted off this mortal plane for good at that moment and I would not have struggled. This was a gift from God; Abba's love was surging through my cells like nothing I had felt before. I began to cry, I sobbed, I was so overwhelmed by his love. I was up another level, 1826 this time, when will this end?

11. 16th Sept 2008 – My Next Planet (1856)

Today's cleansing was pretty much as usual, my guide Andrew took me back to the crystal city. As I opened the lid of the casket, I could see a thick line of light from top to bottom. At six points there were lines coming out from the central column, one left and one right. I climbed inside and the light filled my spine and brushed through me in layers, it was very sensual in a way; almost erotic. As the light permeated my every cell, a vortex opened beneath the soles of my feet and it began to suck out the contaminated energy from my body, like a vacuum cleaner. Plates of light moved from above my head and into my crown, then one after another right down through my whole body each one playing a musical note as it moved through me.

By the time it had finished I felt euphoric, I climbed out of the casket and I was completely transparent and opalescent. I passed my fingers through my left arm and I was made of diamond energy that flowed like liquid and then reformed to its original shape. This felt really divine. My new level was 1856 and as I walked over to Andrew, I began to shape shift into a Princess and he looked like a Prince. We silently walked hand in hand over the ocean bed for a while and then made our way back to the garden. I kissed Andrew goodbye and asked Willow if the planet needed any work doing on it. He said that there were a few ET's but lots of excess male energy that needed clearing. I made my way back inside my physical body and called on Lady Nada and the Karmic Board, and got to work. The first net was full of black scrap metal, the second had a few ET's in it, a 1000 or so, and the third was all full of dust and shadows; negative emotions mainly.

I give thanks to my divine helpers and just as I was about to call it a day, Archangel Michael called my name and informed me that I attained another level and needed to go to see the Divine Director for my next initiation. I was about to be given a new planet to take care of. We hastily made our way to the retreat and sure enough the Council was gathered and the Divine Director asked me to approach him. My crown was encrusted with another large diamond and I was awarded custody of a second planet; Orion to be precise. As I accepted my new responsibilities and turned to walk towards the doorway, the whole room echoed with the sound of applause, I was getting used to this now and I held my head up high and nodded and smiled.

Michael and I walked back along the corridors and I made my way home. I needed to ground myself. I was a Planetary Princess responsible for 2 planets. I quickly reminded myself, "You're just a glorified cleaner, Janine, just a glorified cleaner!". This soon grounded me and pulled the rug from under my Princess slippers. A cleaner indeed, I chuckled and

28

pondered what to make my son for dinner. Back to reality!

12. 17th Sept 2008 – The Anchor in my Heart

I woke up with heartburn this morning and I couldn't shift it using the nets. I thought it may have been additives and preservatives, but it wasn't. As I lay in my morning bath water, I suddenly had an image of my first love in my mind. Then I realised that this blockage in my heart chakra must be related to him; strangely enough it was his birthday today, if my memory served me correctly. I set my intentions on removing any and all negative connections to him, and sure enough I could feel a huge rusty anchor being removed from my chest by my Angels. It had black slime dripping from it - this was over 20 years old. I really loved him and when he ended our relationship I was broken hearted. We were sixteen when we started dating and it lasted nearly four years. He was a lovely lad, the boy next door type. You would be pleased if your daughter brought him home, put it that way.

As soon as the anchor was removed, the heartburn ceased, but I needed to fill the hole in my chest. I could see a beautiful orb of aquamarine energy coming toward me and settling into the void; unconditional love, divine. I made my way over the bridge and Willow told me to go to the crystal city with Andrew. As I entered the healing casket, I sensed layers of circular light passing through my body in quick succession. I also had my DNA stripped clean and could feel the reprogramming take place, lots of microscopic geometric symbols made of light entered the cells. It was beautiful and I felt like an angel, I was so clear. 1876 came to mind, I was climbing higher by the day. Later that morning I decided to cut back the bushes and the tree from in front of the house. It's

29

amazing how you lose yourself when you're gardening. I filled three large bins with branches and leaves and had been out for nearly four hours.

Once I had finished in the garden I decided to go and fill my car up with petrol. On the way to the garage I was spotting 666 everywhere. This was a call to service and later that evening I was back in my tub. Pretty much as soon as I closed my eyes I could see three dead stumps and black roots. The roots were being pushed up from the ground as if an unknown force was spitting them out of the planet. I tried to collect them in nets but they were intertwined and had too good a grip on the land. I remembered my sword, the one the Divine Director told me would cut through anything. I held up my right arm and it emerged from my hand.

I chopped up the roots like a chef would cut up carrots. Easy, this was just what I needed, and then net by net the rubbish was removed. When I asked Abba what it was, I was informed that it was mankind's negative thought forms that had contaminated the earth and the land. Once cleaned, I asked Abba and the angels to fill the gaps with exactly what was needed, and layer upon layer of crystal shards descended on me, one on top of the other, like a crystal lasagne, it was delicious.

13. 18th Sept 2008 – The Crown Diamond (1926)

My trip to the crystal city involved me lying inside a body bag, inside the casket today. The bag was zipped closed and inside was the most brilliant golden white light, it was opalescent. As I lay engulfed in this heavenly concoction, I began to absorb the light. Once filled, the zip was undone and before I could get out, my genetic blueprint rose from my being. It was a crystal clear intense of blue. I had only seen this once before in a book called 'Hands of Light' by Barbara Ann Brennan. It was 3 or 4 metres ahead of me before it realised we were detached, then it stopped and we merged together again. How weird was that? 1907, my new calibration. It was high and a part of me was frightened of making a mistake at this level, knowing that my karma would be so severe if I did something wrong. Archangel Michael reminded me that I had reached a new mile stone and needed to visit the chamber at the Royal Teton retreat. White Bear turned up and I popped myself onto the carpet and in an instant we were there. As I walked along the stone walled corridors I remember thinking that all of this attaining was fine, but what was I really letting myself in for? I didn't know and it was probably best that I didn't.

I walked into the chamber, greeted Council and instead of sitting down I walked straight over to the Divine Director. He was holding my new diamond and he placed it firmly in my crown. It was at that point he asked me to remain pure until I had reached 2000. Steven was working away so pure was not a problem, I was virtually celibate anyway. The Council stood and clapped as I gave thanks and made my way out of the chamber. Celibacy, I bet that was the catch. I was only 43, I did not want to be celibate, not for good anyway. I needed to think about that one for a while, and then speak to Abba.

I felt tearful all morning and by late afternoon I was sobbing like a baby. It was the anniversary of my nephew's death next weekend and I felt really low and emotional. The clinic I worked in was under new management, and I didn't cope well with change. I felt sorry for myself and I cried on and off for 3 hours. I was exhausted. I was obviously clearing old emotional stuff from my system and later that evening I lit my candles in the bathroom and had a nice relaxing soak in the bath. There was a huge egg around the outside of my aura, the layer I refer to as 34. It was crusty rock and a dirty brown colour. I asked Archangel Michael to cut it in half and the angels took it away. I was still clearing toxins from my body more or less every day. The down side of being so pure was that everyday pollution really contaminated me. I had to keep on top of my cleansing to feel clear. Once I had done my clearing, Michael told me I had reached 1926.

14. 19th Sept 2008 – Altered Meridians

I had stuff to do early today and missed my morning meditation. Taking my son to college, shopping for paper for the printer, posters to get made for the event I was arranging at a bar in town. I was all over the place and by the time I got round to my clearing, it was 9pm.

My healing session took place in the white room this evening. Abba and Sananda were to remove more implants. I could see them open my aura like I was a flip top toy. They both carefully removed 3 implants from my base that looked like keys. Apparently, this would allow more light to be anchored through me. I could feel Kryon enter the room. He was the being who was responsible for the magnetic field on the planet. He appeared as 2 large sofa sized hands which looked like shiny chrome. He placed one above my head and the other below my feet and pulled my meridians outwards, allowing me to ground myself more easily. Most people's magnetic field goes down the centre of their body. Mine now went around the outside allowing the light to come through me and ground easier. I felt much better afterwards, 1946 by the end of the session.

32

15. 20th Sept 2008 – My Third Planet (1952)

My level rose to 1952 today after clearing my chakras and aura. Michael reminded me that I was to receive another initiation. We laughed and teased one another as we walked the long stone walled corridor to the chamber. He really felt like my brother, - we were on a level pegging so to speak. He always treated me like I was his equal; what a beautiful product of creation Michael is, a shining example of perfection.

We made our way into the chamber, greeted the Council and I approached the Divine Director. He placed another diamond in my crown, the 4th in fact. I was also awarded responsibility for Sirius as well as Orion and Urantia. Three planets to take care of; no problem, I could do that. I asked Council to help me perform a clearing on the planets and we got to work. By the end of the session, my soul count was up to 757,000. We were all doing well and everyone clapped and applauded one another.

16. 23rd Sept 2008 – One Million Souls

My son had been talking about a moped he wanted all the way to college; it was called a DNA Gilera. The universe always found a way of getting the messages to me. This one meant that I needed to cleanse myself and work on reprogramming my DNA. When I was removing the net from my body I could see sand in it - well, it resembled sand, I'm not really sure what it was but it was no good to me, that I did know.

After my reprogramming session, I made my way up to the white room to find Abba and Sananda chatting. Sananda's energy was so pure, I always felt like a novice in his company; not in a bad way. I was fortunate to have had him as a mentor and missed his presence around me. Abba said he wanted me to work with them to clear lost souls from a neighbouring universe. We worked on one hundred inhabited planets and netted 265,000 souls in all, it was unbelievable, such power and results, what results! This meant that my total was 1,020,000, I had exceeded the million, I couldn't believe it, to be honest.

17. 24th Sept 2008 – Empress Initiation (2000)

Something gave me the feeling a major event was going to take place today, not just my initiation but on a cellular level. Archangel Michael guided me to the white room, he carried me up the 33 flights of crystal stairs to save my energy. I was about to hit 2000, pretty good for a human, I knew I was the first to achieve it. I greeted Abba and he asked me to lie on the crystal table. Suddenly the table was gone. I was floating in mid air and I was aware of a large cog type implant, like a wheel in a mill. It was part of me and about 6ft across. Abba guided it out with his hands and the angels took it away. I've changed, my essence, my whole body. I looked like a small universe, galaxies and planets inside a clear space, shaped like a human body. The outside of the form was made of various high vibrational colours like silver, gold and white. I could see a small group of stars inside my torso like a miniature galaxy of planets and stars. I had transformed from the previous diamond coloured clear being with prismatic qualities, to a being that was so clear, it looked like I was formed from space itself; unless I moved I was completely camouflaged, I looked like the surrounding universe.

I was informed that I was the first incarnate being to achieve this level on Earth. It had taken a lot of work and self sacrifice. Even though I felt wonderful, I still needed a rest, as mentally I was low on energy. I wanted to go to sleep. Abba told me to rest and return this evening for my initiation. Once dried and dressed I slept like a baby for two hours: this was unusual for me until recently. I always found it impossible to sleep in the day time but I was out for the count.

That evening I ran myself a warm bath and lit my meditation candle and for a brief moment I was terrified. I had purified my mind, body and soul to the level of Empress of the local universe. I was about to be placed in charge of my local universe, a phenomenal amount of power for any one let alone little old me. All sorts of fears and concerns began to run through my mind. What if I screw up? I'm only human after all. For a moment I was in two minds about accepting the initiation at all. Maybe I should just stick with the three planets and leave it at that.

I remembered the little red headed girl with low self esteem, who only wanted some recognition of her achievements. I was that girl and here is my chance to get some recognition of my endeavours, by God, who else mattered? I had to go; of course I had to go. Not turning up would be like refusing your hard earned gold medal at the Olympics; madness, utter madness. So I decided to go and accept my crown. I could only do my best, and fingers crossed it would be good enough.

I made my way silently along the stone corridors to the main chamber. Abba, Sananda, the Divine Director, the Karmic Board and even the eighth Dimensional Galactic Masters were seated in a circular format around the room. As I entered the room, they all stood up and began to clap, I felt so humble; I was ecstatic and terrified all at once. My old fears tortured me as I walked toward the Divine Director, Abba and Sananda. Once the applause ceased Abba stepped forward and removed my old crown. Sananda then handed his crown to Abba. It looked large and heavy, it was gold and fit for a king. I looked at it and thought, "No way is that going to fit me, it will end up around my neck."

The Divine Director voiced my new obligations and contractual responsibilities regarding my personal behaviour, and the local universe. I was oblivious, my mind rambling on about the crown being too big.

I remember thinking "Shut up, you stupid woman and listen!" My heart was racing as Abba lifted the crown and held it above my head barely touching my hair. Problem solved! As soon as the crown felt my essence it began to shape shift, remoulding into a beautiful three layered tiara encrusted with diamonds. I became at peace as Abba placed it on my head, a perfect fit, of course.

(Although I had accepted my new status as Empress of the local universe I still had reservations).

18. 23th Sept 2008 –
Day 1 Empress of Local Universe.

I called over to my friend's house today. Tess was the one person who knew my calibration. I could tell her anything and I trusted she would believe me, I don't know what I could have done without her at times, I was telling her all about my new level and that she could lessen her karmic debt by working a certain way. While we chatted I drank a glass of non alcoholic wine she insisted I try. It was okay, a little sweet but it felt like we were toasting my success and seemed apt.

I told her about a client of mine who had called me last night to say she had broken 26 contracts she had made prior to her incarnation with some rather naughty extraterrestrials. Tess realised it was a message to let me know my spiritual contracts were now void and new things awaited me. I was not sure where my life was going, to be honest. She gave me the half full bottle of wine to take home, and I did drink one more glass.

I went to see the Divine Director and agreed to the new contract and made some personal requests at the same time. I'd spent so much of my time on my spiritual development that I had lost a part of myself, the part of me that likes to play and have fun. I was so serious, I began to annoy myself. I needed to give my inner child some attention.

19. 26th Sept 2008 – Talking in School

I was expecting Steven about 11am; we were going away for a couple of days to Yorkshire. At 9am he called to say we couldn't go and I was so upset. I needed a break and with him working away so much our time together was limited. He said he would come over and we could go for lunch. So we decided to go to Woodstock, a lovely little place in Oxfordshire. While we were driving along he received a call from his daughter's school saying that she had been put on report for talking in class; then she rang and said she was talking about science in her science class. Their new teacher was upset about it and put her on report. Steven was annoyed at the over reaction of the teacher and we had to pull into a service station in order for him to make a call to the school. He found it difficult over the loud speaker in the car, and I did too. As he was walking up and down talking to his daughter, I started to think what was the mirror showing me, what was being reflected

37

here. I soon realised that I was in trouble for telling Tess too much, Earth was our school and I had a tenancy to help people a little too much rather than letting them learn the hard way, like I had too. Once the drama was over we were on our way, and after a brief walk around Woodstock we had a lovely lunch in a restaurant in the main street.

Almost as soon as we sat down I developed a headache; by the time we left the restaurant I felt terrible. I really needed to lie down. A large white van drove past me with a green arrow and the word HOME written on it. It was a sign telling me to go home, I noticed a Vespa moped with a target painted on it and a shop sign saying "well spotted". I asked Steven to take me home and when he left I had a look to see what was happening. I could see a target on top of my head and a 3ft long arrow sticking out of my crown, no wonder I had a headache. This was my anger at being let down; it had attracted more rubbish and bang! Shot me in the head. I must try to think happy thoughts even when I am down but it is so hard at times.

20. 27th Sept 2008 – Lord Thoth

For some reason I have been cleaning like crazy, the house, the car even the shampoo bottles, the little jobs I usually quite happily over look. While I was cleaning the word Thoth kept coming into my mind. I had been sent a message saying that I was getting a new guide but Thoth was a god, surely he would be too important to guide me. My higher self advised me to remove the rods from my spine, so later I settled down to clear myself and find out who my new Guide was.

The rods come out easily, my spine then filled up with beautiful upside down pyramids of light, from top to bottom. The top had formed a cup shape and had a crystal ball in it. When this was settled in, I was called to the white room. I always worried when I was summoned. I asked Michael if I had made a mistake or was I in trouble? He just smiled and said no. We flew up the centre of the crystal staircase and there was a man standing at the door. Thoth came into my mind again, it was him; what was this all about? We both walked into the room and Archangel Michael stood outside waiting for me. I sat down, Thoth stood to my right, then Abba appeared, first as a white galaxy and then as a man.

I sat quietly waiting for instructions or something. Abba calmly informed me that Thoth, the God of the seven Havona worlds was my new Guide. I was being trained to take back my title of Goddess. I was to call him Lord Thoth. What a shock that was. I felt like I had handed in the keys to my Mini and been given the keys to a Ferrari. 3000 was the level of a Goddess. I asked why I had not been told this before and Abba said that it would have worried me if I knew who I really was. Thoth was my father; I was the reincarnation of the Goddess Artemis from the Havona worlds, who volunteered to come back to Earth and help with the ascension of the planet. Was I really a Goddess, I can't be, this was too much, I needed time to absorb it.

Lord Thoth referred to me as Serena, this was my angel name. I was advised to use it instead of Janine of Warwick, as it would grant me rites of passage throughout the higher Havona worlds and give me access to greater spiritual teachings. I was already being tutored at level 4 Havona training because of my achievements on Urantia and the local Universe. I now had the knowledge that enabled me to work on one hundred inhabited planets at a time. I didn't really think it was a big deal but I wasn't human any more, I was a galactic human, a new species.

I was grateful for the news, but a little shocked and apprehensive. I needed to let the information grow on me. I left the room and Michael and I transported ourselves back to the bottom of my garden. I turned and looked at Willow.

"So now you know" he said and that was all. I silently found myself lying in a cool bath, my head in a daze.

21. 28th Sept 2008 - Road Rage

While I was driving to and from my mother's house today, I heard sirens and alarms going off all over the place. I've seen two accidents and a road rage incident, all in a twenty five minute journey. It looked like the world was going mad. At 8pm I decided to journey to see Abba. Sananda was sitting with him in the white room. I told them about the aggressive energy I had witnessed today, and the three of us carried out a huge clearing on the local universe; the nets were full of ETs, anger, greed, black rocks and worms.

22. 29th Sept 2008 – Reach out and touch Faith

I had received a message to visit my teacher and made my way to see Lord Thoth, he was in the white room with Abba. He wanted to know how I was coping with the news of my origins.

"No problem" I said.

It really felt fine with me. We carried out another quick clearing on Urantia, Orion and Sirius and collected 12,000 lost souls. The total was 1,075,000 in all. This system worked so well it was fantastic really. I was lucky to have been taught it in the first place. Archangel Michael was to praise for my tuition, he is brilliant.

I then got to work clearing the toxins and pollutants from my body, my calibration went up to 2026. I thanked them for helping me and made my way home.

Later that evening, I felt like I had something stuck in my spine again and needed to do some more work on myself. As the rods were removed and my spine was cleaned, I could see more geometric shapes made of light coming into my crown and stacking up one on top of the other, they were square this time. I wonder what they had encoded in them. I guess I would find out eventually. I removed a chip from my heart chakra which was causing me heartburn symptoms, and I felt much better - 2076.

I have had a quiet couple months, not many clients, a few students and I have made a couple of lovely new friends. I was so engrossed in writing, astral travelling and keeping myself clear that I hadn't taken notice of my increasing credit card statement, and when it arrived I was filled with panic. How am I going to pay this? I was being drawn into the money trap and I couldn't stop myself from worrying about it.

I needed to get this fear of lack out of my body, I was going downhill rapidly. My friend offered a free massage treatment and I was happy to accept. As she moved her hands to the back of my solar plexus there was a crack, and I could feel some relief, but more needed to be done. There were these beautiful angels standing to my left and they placed a golden orb into the gap in my stomach, it felt cool but heavy.

I felt calmer but later on I needed to do some more work on myself. I went to sleep for two hours when I got home. I was unconscious, no dreaming, nothing. I was out of my body, but where, I had no recollection at all.

At 9pm I lay in a warm bath and the room was lit only with a single candle, I had better visuals in these conditions. As I pulled the light nets out of my body with the intention of removing fear, I could see a sand like substance covering my liver and kidney. My oracle cards had mentioned letting go of fear earlier, it was hard to let go at times, but the nets seemed to be removing it.

Once I had cleared as much as I could, I lay in the water and I began to cry, I sobbed, money was a pain, I needed to sort it out. My son was in the other room and I noticed the lyrics of the song were "Reach out and touch faith" by Depeche Mode.

All of a sudden an angel appeared right there in front of me; it was the angel Faith. Reach out and touch Faith. I reached out my hand and she held it. I was engulfed with golden rays of light, like a whirlpool, they surrounded my body. It was faith, I was being given more faith. I stayed in that position until the song stopped playing in the background and made my way to the white room. On the floor was a key and tiny treasure chest. I opened the chest and took out a cheque - a cheque for £33 million. Is this a trick? I panicked and gave the cheque to my Guardian Angel requesting he took it to Abba, and asked him to give it to whoever deserved it the most. Why I did that I have no idea. I lay there for a few minutes saying to myself. "You idiot, you just refused a cheque for £33 million, what's wrong with you?"

Five minutes later Abba appeared cheque in hand. I asked him to hang on to it, and only to give it to me if I really deserved it. I know I did but it was a lot of money and it scared me.

23. 2nd Oct 2008– A Quiet Day

All I can say about today is that it was quiet. I really feel the need to spend some time alone. If I was going to win the lottery, a lot of people were going to expect some major handouts, and this money was being given to me to help light workers, and it was vital I handled it correctly. My oracle cards told me to thank God for abundance as it would speed up the manifestation. So thank you was my daily mantra.

I decided to stay home and read a book, a neighbour had lent me. It was written by Professor Jane Plant, and called 'Your life in your hands'. She was a scientist who had developed breast cancer in 1987. By 1993 it had spread to her lymph system. Alongside her medical treatment she used diet and simple life changes that not only shrank the tumour, but over came her dis-ease.

24. 3rd Oct 2008 – Pink Moon Leeches

Today I decided to concentrate on clearing the planet. I settled into a warm bath and called for the help of my little pink moon leeches. The angel who was their Guardian appeared to my right side with the little box of miracle workers in her hands. She opened the box and I asked the leeches if they would go into the sea and clear as much of the pollution away as possible. I could see the planet about the size of a football in front of me and the angel helped the leeches out of the box and into the sea. They enthusiastically swam around absorbing the pollution from oil spillage and the fuel that was emptied into it from aeroplanes.

In a matter of minutes they were all black and the job was done. They hopped out, into the magic box, and were instantly clean, clear, and transformed into the pure beings they were initially.

I blew them a kiss and the energy turned into little pink birds and butterflies, which flew into their sweet pure hearts. The sea looked so clear, it was sparkling. The fish looked happy and there was a calmness which spread to the very core of the planet. Mother Earth thanked me for thinking of her, and I went about my day.

25. 5th Oct 2008 – Relationships End

Last Tuesday I removed fear of lack from my body and good things started to happen. Steven told me to go and get some new taps for my bathroom and tiles; he said he would treat me to them. Work has been slow recently and money was a bit of a problem, but it seemed that the more I ignored it the worse it got. I was over drawn at the bank and I had lots on a credit card, not good at all really.

Over the last few days, lots had happened. I kept being told by Abba not to worry about money and Faith had surrounded me in her light. Later that evening and twice the next day I kept hearing the word lottery or seeing it on TV. It felt like I was being sent a message. When I asked my guides if I was going to win the lottery I was told "Yes, in three weeks time". I didn't believe it, though, who would! My son came home from college and told me his EMA payments would be held up until Christmas, instead of the three weeks he had been told previously, a government mistake. This also felt like a message.

44

The suspense was killing me and I took the lift to the white room to speak to Abba. He told me that I would win the lottery at Christmas. I could see a cheque in his hands and peered over to see that the date was Christmas 2009 another year away. I needed some help now. I put my arms around him and asked him like a child asking her father for a pony; "Please change the date on the cheque Father, please", and he said he would think about it.

Apparently the Time Lords from the 11th dimension had made a mistake with the creation of my lottery win. I was flabbergasted; I was going to win the lottery. Six months ago while I was meditating, a cheque for £33 million floated down from the sky and I caught it, but I didn't think it would really manifest. £33 million was written on a cheque from me to me in a building society savings book in my bedroom drawers, had I really manifested such an enormous win? Time would tell.

The next day, Thursday, I took my son to college and as I walked into the garage shop to pay for my petrol I noticed a newspaper head line saying, "Can we fix it? Yes we can." I felt sure it was Abba letting me know that the Time Lords had changed creation, and the date on the cheque. As I drove out of the garage, a white Audi R8 was opposite me, I associate them with a lottery win, so this was another positive sign. I felt really happy and my mind was at peace.

When I got home I had a quick look on my computer for any new emails, another way Abba contacted me and there was a message saying "What is your life purpose?" I figured my spiritual contract was about to be altered and I ran the bath immediately and made my way to the retreat to find out what this involved. Archangel Michael told me not to worry, that the contract was not anything I was not already complying with. I would be fine.

The Divine Director reminded me that I was to eat only pure foods, no sugar or grain or dairy. No swearing, no talking ill of people, and to press on with my spiritual work. I was only to submit to the pleasures of the flesh now and then, and to purify myself afterwards.

"I accept this new contract". I replied and I was told that I would win £33 million on the lottery and to use it to help light workers, and to spread the word regarding self healing and enlightenment. I was to be awarded a sum to purchase a new property and a car. I was to use some of the money to pay my living expenses. I could do this easy.

I watched secret millionaire on TV last week where a millionaire joins working class communities and donates large sums of money to worthy causes. I said out loud "I wish I could do that". Abba must have granted my wish. I agreed to the terms and conditions, and made my way home.

A part of me still questioned whether this was real or not. I had experienced a lot of disappointments recently. My 1st book was rejected by the publisher and I was supposed to go away for the weekend last weekend with Steven, but it was cancelled and I had really been looking forward to it. I need to carry out a clearing on myself and I was hoping this was not going to be another disappointment. We had changed the hotel to this weekend instead. I was in need of a rest and so was he.

It was Friday morning, I had dropped my son off at college and was all packed and ready to go when Steven phoned me to say he felt a bit off and that he

46

was going to go back to bed for a couple of hours, and that he would call me later and we could head off then. All dressed up and nowhere to go, I sat down and started to day dream about what I could do with £33 million; I could help so many people. I wanted a retreat in the country, a silent retreat. I soon fell asleep on the couch. Steven called at 3.20pm and said that he was too ill to travel, and I told him to cancel the hotel and rest. I was so upset, this was a sign, I knew it. I cried for a while. I had already been told that I could not fulfil my destiny if I stayed with him and later I called Tess to talk to her about it. It was getting embarrassing, so many last minute let downs and empty promises, I was pretty low and I decided to sleep on it. Things always looked better in the morning. We decided it was a lesson in acceptance of God's Will.

I woke up early on Saturday morning and lay in bed thinking about my relationship, and what I should do. Then I just made the decision, it had to end. I needed to be free to get on with my work. An hour later Steven called and I tried to explain that I was finding it all too upsetting and emotionally draining. I'm sure he was expecting it. He realised that he was causing me stress and said that he would stop calling me. I felt a bit sick inside, but also relieved. Ten minutes later Jules called and I was talking to her about it all, she said it was sad but probably for the best, I did spend a lot of time waiting around for him because he was so busy, time that could be better spent elsewhere.

Later that day I received another initiation; a gem stone was placed in my breastplate. I had reached 2103 but I wasn't in the mood for celebration. That night I dreamt about a dark man who was travelling around covering my students and clients in a grey cloud of smoke. When I woke up this morning I did a clearing on them as a group; it was excess male energy and dense. I rang Jo and let her know about it; she said she had felt a bit low and heavy over the last few days, and thanked me for keeping her up to date. The conversation soon evolved into my relationship breakdown. Jo knew I was broke and said she would buy one of my books, bless her.

Today was my brother's birthday; he died nearly 2 years ago. I called his name three times and wished him a happy birthday, but I could not see him.

Later I had a quick look in the craft stop as I was thinking about making my own Christmas cards. I was looking at a whole section full of signs, and the one I read said, "It is better to have loved and lost than never loved at all". At that moment I knew my brother was with me. He once told me that, over twenty years ago, when my first love finished with me. I said hello and told him I missed him. When I went into the car park I saw a number plate with MIKE 1 on it and I smiled, it was him all right, that was his name, I could feel him near me.

I left the shopping centre and went to see my mum. My sister was there and I was updated on my mum's latest drama. She is 84 and not very mobile. She had slid off the side of her bed this morning and was stuck sitting on the floor unable to lift herself up. When her morning carer arrived, she picked her up and all was well, thankfully (she has broken both hips before, in falls). My mum asked the carer to call her sister in Scotland who was hard of hearing and 80 or so herself. She thought my mum was stuck on the floor and rang my cousin to get help, who in turn rang my sister. The phone calls were covering over 500 miles in distance, what a mix up. The stupid thing was that my mum has a panic alarm, but was not wearing it at the time. Everyone was laughing about it now, as no harm was done.

I noticed a car on TV that was called a Focus. My brother was telling me about a guy at his local bar who won £300,000 on the lottery. The penny dropped. I was only getting £300,000 not £33 million. I could hardly save the world with that amount. What had happened? As I drove over to my son's father's house I asked what was wrong, and I got the reply that I had been talking about Steven in a negative way and had blown my lottery win as a consequence. My mum mirrored me falling, the phone calls had represented the wise ones discussing my fate, and the Focus car was to let me know about the money being less. My heart sank to the floor. I saw three traffic cones in a bush and that meant that I had been given three chances, Tess, Jules, and Jo. I had spoken to all of them, how stupid of me.

As I drove home in silence, my son could sense a problem and when he asked me what was wrong. I told him I had split up with Steven. He asked me why and I said, "It just wasn't meant to be".

I prayed all of the way home and when I got in, I quickly journeyed to the retreat. Everyone was there and I asked Abba if I had ruined my lottery win and he showed me a cheque for £33 million torn in half and a new one for £300,000. I was gutted and fell to my knees, exhausted and distraught.

Then just as I was about to beg for mercy, my beautiful Fairy Godmother arrived and stood by my side.

"I have come to grant you a wish", she said.

"I wish I could have one more chance". I cried. She waved her wand and covered me in fairy dust.

"Your wish is granted, you deserve another chance. You are a good girl". She smiled like an angel.

As I looked at the torn cheque lying on the floor in front of me, it repaired itself and flew back into Abba's open hand. The other one disappeared.

"Oh, thank you, thank you so much", I sobbed.

Lady Nada walked over to me and said, "Come on Janine, get up, it's OK," I stood up and she hugged me as if I were a child, all wet from the tears and feeling scorned and regretful.

"It will be fine, calm down", she held me tight. I was so distressed I was shaking. Then I thanked my Fairy Godmother and she was gone, as quickly as she had appeared.

My nightmare was over. Lesson learned. Do not gossip even when you are hurting, keep your words pure. I was single again and remembered the mountain telling me these words, "Your fairness is your fate, accept it". I had to keep myself pure in thought, word and deed.

What a stressful encounter that was, time for tea.

26. 6th Oct 2008 - Sound Healing (2117)

Abba told me to stop worrying and to get on with my writing, so this morning I decided to do exactly that. I had at least six weeks of notes that needed writing out properly and I spent the first half of my day sorting out dates and adventures. By the time I had eaten breakfast, it was nearly midday and a warm bath was calling me.

Every day I need to clear my body of toxins, my skin was almost better and I am actually feeling in pretty good shape all round. I made my way over the bridge and sat with Willow for while. He could see that I was a lot happier today.

"Do you think Abba would have really penalised me so much for gossiping?" I asked Willow.

"Gossip is considered a sin and much frowned upon, but I expect you were being taught a very short and sharp, hard lesson" said Willow.

"You're right about that" I replied.

A minute or so later, Andrew arrived to take me for my healing session in the crystal city. We jumped into the pond and swam to our destination. He stood at the door like an armed guard, while I made my way up the crystal steps to the casket. I lifted the lid and could see a kind of mesh birds nest inside. It was brown and smelly. No way was I getting in there.

Abba arrived with a couple of golden Cherubs who promptly removed the mesh and cleaned the casket. I looked at the clear liquid inside and noticed ten tiny whirl pools forming at intermediate points along the length of the box. They grew larger until they were about 4-6 inches in diameter. Then they stopped spinning and looked like glass tubular vases. Abba ushered me into the casket and as I lay down on top of the tubes I realised that they were in exact alignment with my chakras. I was asked to sing a musical note, starting low then changing it to a higher note; a scale like do, ra, me, fa, so, la, te, do. As I did this, the tubes began to play a musical note in unison and they tuned my chakras like a toning fork would. It was fantastic; my every cell was dancing to the song of the miraculous little orchestra.

It felt unbelievable. I was vibrating all over and in a moment, it stopped. I was balanced and scaling 2117. Abba smiled as I climbed out of the box and we silently made our way to the special garden. We didn't talk much; we just sat in the sunshine. I heard an alarm go off outside in the street but I didn't take any notice of it.

About an hour later, I was drinking a cup of tea and thinking about the silence in the garden. It was unusual. Abba always spoke to me when we were together. An alarm was sounding in the distance, three times I heard it. Something was wrong. I called for Archangel Michael and asked him what was going on.

"It was Satan, not Abba, he stole your crystal heart." He told me.

I was usually much quicker at discernment than this; he'd fooled me today. No hard feelings, I pulled my stolen heart crystal back through a portal and Michael placed it firmly in position. All was well again. I should know by now, that alarms are always letting me know some thing's wrong and never to ignore them.

27. 7th Oct 2008 – The £33,000,000 Cheque

Last night a friend came over for a Crystal Ki treatment. While I was working on her heart chakra, I could see what looked like broken glass; it was her heart chakra crystal. The bits were removed and I could see a sort of Rubik cube with three or four small crystal wands growing out of it. It was a dark purple metallic. My Angels told me that it was a chip. It was placed in there by the ETs to steal her love energy; I promptly removed it. My Angelic helpers then

52

replaced it with the most beautiful crystal I have ever placed in a person. It had a diamond ball at the centre; about 2 inches in diameter and six square cut pyramids touching one another; in the centre of the ball, the flat of the pyramid was to the outside giving the overall appearance of a box. As it was placed into the void the chip had made, she could see light radiating from the diamonds and filling her whole body. It was fantastic.

After the treatment, we had a cup of ginger tea and she was telling me that the glass door on her cooker had blown up a few weeks ago. I pointed out to her that it was a 3rd dimensional sign that her heart was damaged because the cooker, being in the kitchen, is considered by many to be the heart of the home. She realised I was right and said she would try to think a little more about things in future. I told her not to try too hard, because as you raise your consciousness, you naturally become more aware, but if you invoke the energy of the hawk, you will spot things much quicker, and with ease.

Later (about 10.20pm) I was watching a program with my son on the laptop. He insisted I watch this particular comedy with him. As I was watching it, I noticed the words 'Now 666' pop up on a sign in the background; another call to service. By 10.30pm I was laying in my second bath of the day. Archangel Michael said that that Karmic Board had called me. A problem with lost souls had arisen. I entered the chamber and we began the clearing, there were two planets and we collected over 23,000 in one session.

We also removed greed, anger, deprivation and a lot of muddy brown energy masses created by the amount of humans becoming temporarily possessed by the off world creatures. The chemical reaction caused by solid and spirit coming together forms ectoplasm, which looks like clear jelly, but it's heavy and not nice at all. So we had to clean up Urantia while we were there. Once my work was done I made my way back to my bath tub and I felt the need to remove fear from my body. Not fear of the aliens and demons, but fear relating to taking my place in the world as a spiritual leader. I now realised my destiny was a lot more important than I had previously considered, and to be honest I was scared of making a mistake. I had the powers of an Empress, a whole Universe under my jurisdiction and my own band of angels. I was only human and a mistake at this level could be catastrophic. That was the fear I had inside me. I asked Michael to help me remove it in a net and the angels pulled a small net about the size of a single bed from just below me, and up through my body.

As it rose upwards and left me, it took a body shaped energy away, like a cocoon. It was like every tiny atom of fear was removed from me on a cellular level. I felt like a million dollars, no, a billion dollars. But most of all, I felt at peace; I was peace; I am peace. I could see Abba, he was holding something in his hand; a cheque. He gave it to me, £33,000,000 made payable to Miss J Regan. Even though I was lying down my knees began to tremble as I held out my left hand and said thank you. I didn't know what to do with it so I decided to shrink it down to a micro dot and placed it in my diamond heart, like a tiny flaw you would get in a good quality diamond. Money was impure after all, usually any way.

As quickly as he arrived he was gone again. I lay there thinking about how many people I would be able to help with so much funding from Heaven. This was my ultimate dream scenario. I could spend the rest of my life doing what I enjoyed most, helping people and spreading the word about self healing and global healing awareness. I felt so euphoric, I didn't want this moment to end but the water was cold and it was time for bed.

28. 8th Oct 2008 – The Crystal Ball

Today's clearing was completely weird. I decided to clear my whole auric field right out to level 35. As the grid tried to move through the layers it just surrounded my aura and would not pass through it, as if it were solid. I had two ways of clearing myself, the first was visualising the grid above my head and moving it along horizontally through me as I lay in the bath and the second was viewing myself in the distance as if I was working on someone else; I had better all round vision that way.

I decided to switch from the first technique to the second, and I could see myself trapped inside a crystal ball, quartz in fact. I panned out my vision whilst calling for Archangel Michael and I was shocked to see that I was inside a crystal ball that was being held by a huge being, he looked very much like an old Chinese or Mandarin warrior. When I asked my higher self what was going on, I realised he had captured me during the night. I must have forgotten to close all of my chakras, or something. He had seen my power capacity and placed me inside the ball to use me as an energy source, he was a Sorcerer; I had a problem!

Within seconds Archangel Michael turned up and I asked him to cut me free. He chopped the ball in half and I shot out at warp speed, flew up and landed on his shoulder; I was the size of a bee compared to him.

Michael pointed the tip of his sword at the face of the Sorcerer and warned him that he would suffer the wrath of God if he tried to capture me again. He told him that I was highly protected by the Wise Ones and out of bounds. The Sorcerer looked defiant and turned in disgust at his loss.

"Thanks Michael that was unexpected" I said "He took you when you were asleep; you need to take more care."

"I know, I'm sorry."

The next thing I knew White Bear appeared and we were on our way to the retreat for my next initiation. The Divine Director gave me one more crystal which was placed in my breastplate, and after a round of applause from the Council, I was back on the flying carpet with White Bear and on my way to Mount Shasta.

The wise mountain told me that I needed to be careful as Steven's anger would harm me. I asked what I should do and was told that Abba could place a temporary containment chamber around him, if I requested it. So I did, and rather than get upset at being attacked I asked God to bless, heal and purify the relationship. By the time Steven came over later to collect his things, he was calmer than I expected. The whole situation was sad, but I could not afford to get sucked into wasting my energy on negative situations; I was far too powerful for that.

29. 8th Oct 2008 – Credit Crunch Junk

I noticed a junk email referring to service something or other, and the colour red was jumping out at me, even the red tree in my garden seemed larger than life. I needed to do some more work on the planet. I always see red as a warning; it's base energy and a sign that too much masculine energy is around.

As the Karmic Board worked with me, we pulled a grid through Mother Earth. She had a thick layer of red around her, like treacle. It was being caused by the credit crunch rubbish in the media. People were frightened and angry, and the world was obsessed with money and base thought forms. All of it was producing a thick smog of red energy, which was contaminating the whole globe. The power of the media is shocking, it's all rubbish, a ploy to create more base energy; luckily people like me can remove it. The next net was to remove the anger and greed caused by it. The third net, the excess of base sexual energy. Red also stimulates the sex drive; this causes over sexed, testosterone pumped up youth culture, leading to even more under age sex and violence.

Once we had cleaned it, I made my way up to the white room where Abba was waiting for me. By the time I arrived, my head had half a dozen little daggers sticking out of it (caused by my anger at the situation), and I was covered in a thin layer of red, like a wet suit. I pulled the daggers out and peeled the wet suit off in one piece. Abba asked me to come and sit with him. He said that by tomorrow I would hit a new land mark and another implant would be removed. I could see the implant it was like a wire flower, lilly shaped with gems on it. Abba held out a small marble sized orb on a tiny stick of light.

"What's this?" I asked as he gave it to me.

"It's a light lollipop" he replied.

Without hesitation or doubt I swallowed it whole. The most amazing thing happened; my stomach lit up like a beacon; it was warm and comforting. I knew it would settle my nerves and hopefully help me focus on my writing; it's been a chore recently.

30. 9th Oct 2008 – My Breastplate (2202)

I decided to leave my initiation to later in the day, as I could see better at night when I was journeying and I didn't want to miss anything. I felt tired today and found it difficult to settle down and write. Something was wrong but I wasn't sure what.

When I checked my chakras, my brow chakra was broken and I could see two hypodermic needles about 2 feet long sticking in my head and neck. I removed them and repaired the damage. My headache went away instantly. I soon realised that this was an alien assault (my thoughts must have attracted it). Typical of the sort of weapons they use; so I did a quick clean up on the planet before going to see Abba, to have my implant removed.

As I lay on the healing table in the white room, Abba simply placed his hand inside my throat and removed it; to be honest, it looked more like a tiny metallic chandelier than a lily, when it was out. Abba told me that this would make my words more powerful; he said I should always think before I spoke. I now understood why I was taught such a harsh lesson about gossip last weekend.

My body now calibrated at 2202; three two's meant dreams come true. I hope so, I really do. He told me I needed to visit the chamber and we both walked through the doorway which usually led us into the garden, but we were at the retreat. Straight through a worm hole, this holographic matrix was beyond words.

I made my way over to the Divine Director and after congratulating me he placed a large diamond in my breastplate, right in the centre where my heart was.

The diamond was about 3 inches in diameter. It touched the breastplate and fused itself into position, lines of gold grew from it and crawled outwards like the roots of a tree, over the surface of my armour. The lines formed a perfect eight pointed geometric, shaped like a star.

"This will protect you, Janine of Warwick, nothing will penetrate this shield." I was told.

It mirrored its form on the back of my body as well. I was sealed, my heart protected. I was over whelmed with gratitude and I had tears in my eyes. I remember thinking I wish my mum and dad were here to see this.

31. 10th Oct 2008 – My Mistake

I had a dream last night, I could only remember bits of it when I woke up, but they were enough for me to get the message. First of all my son's pet tarantula spider died in the dream; she was running around like an athlete one minute, and then she got trampled on. This meant my creative energy was damaged. In the dream I could see a white car with the name Spock (an alien/ human life form from a Star Trek movie) on the number plate, in black on a yellow background. Black was not good energy and yellow was my solar plexus, stomach area. If this is blocked it is difficult to focus. Next, I was given a electric convector heater but the plug had been cut off. This represented my main power cable down from source, my governor meridian.

When I tuned in and had a look, I could see that the meridian was completely severed just below my heart, and there was a vortex type chip in my stomach. No wonder I didn't feel like writing and was so tired.

59

I called in my divine helpers and watched as the little Angels fused the broken wires back together, repairing the sheath and removing the chip. I felt a lot better and once I had drunk my tea, I was writing again and enjoying it, thanks to my little Cherubs. I love you guys.

I was driving down to Oxfordshire about an hour away from my home, to see a friend of mine for a chiropractic adjustment. When I had a lot of work on and was being attacked by the lower frequency ET's, I sometimes become a bit adrenal and off balance. My hip would tilt slightly causing lower and upper back ache. It had been one of those days when you can't switch your mind off, and I had a blinding headache.

As I was driving along the motorway, I saw three large signs with Clarkson on (my Chiropractor's name) and then I saw three large red lorries. Red usually meant stop. I was so in my own head, that I took no notice of it and carried on. When I got within the last couple of miles of her clinic, I got totally lost. I had been at least half a dozen times before, and no problems. It was as if the road signs had been moved or something.

I soon realised what was going on when my CD turned itself off and the radio came on instead. I heard the words "GO AWAY" and clicked back into reading my 3d signs. I said "Okay I'll go home", and sensed my Spirit Guides cheering as if to say, she's got the message at last. When I asked what was wrong, a car pulled in front of me with VVV on the number plate. V's always meant dark warrior ET's to me. She must have one attached to her; they were everywhere this week - it was tiresome.

For some reason I burst into tears and cried for the whole journey home; my headache eased a little as a result. When I got back I contacted Tess to see if she could help, she said she would squeeze me in over the weekend. I felt low and by 9pm my lymph glands in my groin were tender. I must be fighting an infection as well as all of this emotional and mental stuff I'm clearing. I couldn't stop thinking about the lottery and what if I made a mistake and it was cancelled. I would have let everyone down and I would be flat broke. I prayed for help. I was terrified and I couldn't control my thoughts.

I needed to sort it out, so I ran myself a bath and set my intentions of pulling out fear of lack, fear of making a mistake, and anything else that would hold me back. Before I knew it, I was carrying out a soul retrieval, on myself. This involves finding a part of your soul, lost because of a trauma; a fragment of your personality. In this case, my inner child and restoring it back into my heart chakra. It can be very difficult to do especially alone, as you can feel the child's emotions, your own, at reliving the trauma and trying to pacify all parties, I always asked my higher self or Guardian Angel to help and to mediate where necessary.

I could see burnt bodies, five corpses, two adults and three teenagers lying on the street outside of a large three storey house, it was in a smart street. I was standing in the road with a servant holding my hand, I looked about 4 or 5 years old, dressed in the sort of clothes Oliver Twist would wear. The servant, Alice, was holding me tightly and saying "It's okay Peter, it was a mistake, an accident". I was crying and shouting for my mother.

Apparently, I had been playing on the landing at the foot of the stairs to the 2nd floor; my parents and siblings were on the 3rd floor in their rooms preparing for dinner; it was dark outside. Whilst playing, I knocked a candle over and it set alight to the drapes. Frozen in panic, I just stood and watched as the fire took hold and filled the stairwell with thick smoke. The next thing I knew I was in the servant's quarters and we were screaming, there was smoke all over the house. Three servants and the house keeper managed to get out in time, and they took me with them. The rest of my family were trapped upstairs and they all died; the smoke got to them first, then the flames. It was 1786 and fires were killers; by the time help arrived, it was too late.

As I lay in the bath watching this I was sobbing, my body was shaking in the water, I could feel myself (Peter), I could feel his torment. A mistake, I killed my family, who could love someone like that, was going through my mind. Enough, I'd seen enough and the image and memory was removed from my body.

I pulled myself together and set about finding Peter. Michael had only mentioned to me a couple of weeks ago about how serious I was, and at the time I remember feeling like my inner child was gone, a part of me was missing and here was my chance to fix it. I took some deep breaths and a few minutes later I could see an image of a cage in my base chakra, the fight or flight zone which seemed apt. There I was, all huddled up in the corner of the cage, head in hands, in the dark.

"Hello Peter" I said gently. He looked up at me.

"I've come to take you home, it's all safe now". I opened the door to the cage and moved back. I didn't want to push things.

"I made a mistake" he whispered.

"I know sweetheart, we all make mistakes sometimes, and it was an accident, not your fault. Accidents happen"

"Does God hate me?" he cried.

"God asked me to come and find you, he said to tell you that he loves you and your family are safe and happy in Heaven with him."

"Really?"

"Yes, really, come on, it's okay".

At this point things can go either way, but luckily Peter jumped up and ran enthusiastically into my open arms. I held him so tight I could feel his little heart beat, and the next thing I knew he was back where he belonged inside my heart, wrapped in a pink blanket, an angel by his side. The whole experience was exhausting and I thanked the angels for helping and went to bed.

32. 11th Oct 2008 – Osirus, the Giant Eye

I didn't sleep well last night, I never do when I've been crying; it knocks me off balance temporarily until things settle back down. It can take fourteen days for a soul fragment to settle in and it's important to play and have fun when the fragment is a child.

I ran myself a warm bath and cleaned my body of toxins, radiation and the usual pollution caused by life. My calibration hit 2252, so another initiation was due. Archangel Michael and I flew to the retreat, and before we went inside I grew to the same size as him and not the usual smaller me. It felt right, and we walked along the stone corridors towards the chamber like a couple of buddies, laughing and chatting.

Once inside we took our seats and greeted Council. The Divine Director called me over to him and placed a large gold chain around my neck like a Lord Major would wear. Lady Nada walked over to me and kissed me on the forehead. She congratulated me and told me not to worry about money. Her kiss meant a lot to me, I would cause her problems, by not being pure in the earlier part of my path. I liked a drink of red wine back then, she would advise me to have only one and I would completely ignore her and have as much as I wanted; she had her work cut out mentoring me. I'm amazed how patient she was with me. Something I was learning to be at the moment.

When we left the retreat Michael said that I was to go to see the Pharaoh to receive some Archangel essence. We made our way to the Sphinx and before we went inside I decided to question Michael. He said Abba asked him to bring me there. I looked up and could see Abba, he told me it was all right and to go with Michael. We walked down the steps and stood before the Pharaoh.

Michael looked up and said, "The Father wishes you to reprogram Janine with Archangel Essence".

The Pharaoh directed me to the chair and the process began. The sunlight came in via a hole in the ceiling and hit a diamond crystal egg on a table in front of me. That refracted the light and it formed a vertical grid cutting me in half; the grid evolved forming the shape of an Archangel much like Michael, but made of light, which merged with my essence. I had huge wings and a sword like Michael's. I drew the sword from its sheath with my right hand, and placed the blade over my shoulder like a soldier would a rifle.

The light ceased and it was done. As I walked over to Michael, I gave a diamond from my heart chakra to the Pharaoh, and he placed it in his brow as usual.

By now I felt invincible and Michael said that he wanted to introduce me to a friend.

"Why do I need Archangel Essence?" I asked.

"It grants you rites of passage through the super universe". He replied.

"Okay". I answered, that was all I needed to know.

We flew up into the universe, and as we came to the edge we popped through a wormhole and we were in the super universe. This was fabulous; I was like a child, full of wonder.

If you try to imagine this universe is like the inside of a ring doughnut hollowed out and the inside wall of the skin has passage ways into an even longer ring doughnut and so on. The larger doughnut, the super universe had lots of little doughnuts inside it, different universes. We were in that one and it was trippy. We flew across to one side of it, and I could see a huge eye, like a frog's eye. It turned out to be our destination.

When we arrived, Michael introduced me to his friend Osirus, he was a giant eye. Compared to me he was the size of England, he had a lovely energy, and an opalescent shimmer. Obviously as he did not have a mouth, all communication was telepathic. He asked me if I could play chess and I said yes.

Then a chess set appeared in front of me, a holographic work of art, and the game began. Ladies first, I made my move. 1 minute 35 seconds later I was beaten, check mate. Michael had a grin on his face like a school boy.

"What are you looking like that for?" I asked him.

"He was showing you mercy, he invented the game, I've been playing him for eons and he still beats me in less than 30 seconds; he wasn't even trying"

"Oh! Thank you Osirus for going easy on me that was thoughtful of you", we all laughed.

Osirus said I was welcome any time and to come back soon. We said good bye and as we made our way back towards the wormhole, to the local universe, a strange creature came towards me. I threw a net around it, as a gut reaction. It was shaped like a blue and yellow tube, with a small head sticking out of the top and about 20 legs.

"It's okay, it's a doughnut worm" said Michael, as it fell though the net and glared at me.

"A doughnut worm?!"

"It's real name has about 36 characters in it and I can't pronounce it, so I call them doughnut worms instead", said Michael.

"Cool, I love it, doughnut worms and eyes that play chess". It was Saturday after all!

33. 12th Oct 2008 – Delegate

Today was beautiful, the sun was shining and I felt at peace even though I wasn't physically 100%, I felt good inside. I didn't have time to meditate this morning. I had visitors, but later in the afternoon I decided to check in with Lady Nada and see what was happening. She said that there were still thousands of extraterrestrials on the loose and with the help of the Karmic Board; we pulled some nets through Mother Earth. 12,000 ET's and another 12,000 or so goblins and sprites in the first two nets. One or two are harmless enough, but in groups they cause all sorts of problems, and can affect people's behaviour, especially youngsters.

I had been told by Abba to delegate and called Jo to see if she could help. She was happy to, and said that she would try to do a clearing at least once a week. A half a dozen women like her, and this planet would be ship shape in no time; but finding people who were as dedicated to their light work as Tess and I was harder than I thought.

Later, I went for a treatment with Tess and she very kindly straightened my spine for me which was the result of too much stress and being a bit overworked. I needed to retreat more when I was clearing fear and stuff from myself. It made me vulnerable and open to attack; and the ET's took every opportunity they could to have a go at me. Let's face it, I caught them in nets and deported them, I wasn't exactly at the top of their Christmas card list!

Tess soon sorted me out and I spent the rest of my evening lying on the couch watching the movie "Ghost", it was one of my favourites. I always cried when I watched it, always.

34. 13th Oct 2008 – The Angel Hope (2264)

Last night I had a dream that I was tipsy. I could see cigarettes and a large bag of sweets in a ruck sack. I realised spirit was letting me know that I needed to clear toxins from my system and once I had finished my cup of tea, I ran myself a bath. I tried to bring a grid down through me from level 35 and once again I had a large crystal ball around me. Where it came from, I did not know, but I asked Michael to break it. I flew out and stood by his side, closely resembling Tinkerbell from "Pinocchio" the children's movie. I decided that I would make my way up to the white room and cleanse myself there instead, it felt safer.

The room was empty so I lay on the healing table and pulled a grid down through me to remove toxins. As it moved through my body I felt a layer of energy being peeled away. It looked like a cactus had formed around me, and was being removed like a banana skin, by the grid. Once the grid passed out of the soles of my feet, the rubbish was bagged up and removed by the angels.

A large white angelic being appeared to my left side, I pulled a net through her to make sure it wasn't Satan, up to his old tricks. It passed straight through her. She came over to me and told me her name was Hope. She thanked me for rescuing her from Pandora's Box where she had been locked away; then she held my left hand in hers. A wisp of crystal light began to leave her hand and coil around my arm and body, surrounding me completely in hope energy, a real gift; hope for a brighter future, not just for me but for mankind. She stayed by my side for a couple of minutes and then let go of me and smiling, she turned to walk away.

As she left the room a large squid appeared above me. I wasn't happy with that and I jumped off the table and asked the angels to catch it in a net. There was an alarm going off outside in the street, as soon as the squid was gone it stopped.

Abba appeared, not before time, and asked me to lie back down on the table. I had just hit 2264 and he wanted to perform a DNA cleansing. I did as he asked and a large glass tube formed around me like a test tube. A grid of light passed from head to foot along the tube, similar to an MRI scan, I guess. Then a net pushed out lots of debris, it looked like chalk dust, it was really fine powder. Once emptied, new light waves passed along the tube and my body looked like it was made of silk threads but they were thin and not very bright at first. Then Abba pressed a button on my forehead and the light got brighter and brighter, as if it had changed from 10w to 100w bulb instantly. Wow! Now I was bright. I sat up and he reminded me to hide my light and to remember Faith and Hope.

The next thing I knew I was swimming with dolphins and whales. They were playing with me as if I was one of them. I swam around with them listening to their songs, and I must have dropped off to sleep. Michael was clicking his fingers to wake me and I was lying in a cool bath. My new level was 2286. I stepped out of the bath and the door bell rang. Typical; I quickly got dressed and was soon grounded.

Later, I was asking for a message and using my oracle cards; whales and dolphins were prominent. The whale was considered a record keeper and it meant that my DNA was about to be changed, but the old programming needed to be removed by Abba, first. I had been to collect my son from his aunt's house and on the way home I felt a lump in my throat, a tightness. About 9pm I decided to lie down on my bed and meditate to see what the problem was. I remembered speaking to two different people today who had confidence issues going on and decided the magic mirror was reflecting that I needed to remove any related self confidence issues from myself. As I removed the net, I was amazed to see so much rubbish in it, there was a double hook in my stomach from an ex boyfriend.

I could see his dark side laughing at me as I removed it and cut all negative ties. I could see a chip in my throat; it looked like a small vortex with a rod through the middle, like an old fashioned spinning top. One of my angels took it out for me, and the tightness I had been feeling was gone. I could see myself flying up to the white room where Abba was waiting for me. He asked me to lie on the crystal table; the test tube surrounded me and reprogrammed my DNA just like before, 2320 WOW! My son was calling me and I was back in my room.

35. 14th Oct 2008 – Beetles Everywhere

Every day I need to clear toxins and pollution from my body and aura, I am so sensitive now, even if I surround myself in protection I can still get contaminated. I need a more reclusive life style, a house in the country away from traffic. I hope I win the lottery and I'm not just imagining all these messages. There was one on my computer last night that said only five days to go, that's a week earlier than I thought. Fingers crossed, no more money worries, what a relief that'll be.

As I carried on with my clearing in the bath as usual, I sensed a small creature out of the corner of my left eye, it looked like a beetle. My son was telling me about a game on the PC where a large extraterrestrial being, twice the size of a human, was laying eggs and producing hundreds of thousands of beetle type creatures. Sure enough, there were hundreds of them in my aura. I had picked them up when I was on the telephone earlier. I soon netted them and I also cleared a dark cloud from my left groin which was causing my lymph glands to swell.

The voids were filled with a beautiful prism of light and I flew like a rocket up to see Abba in the white room to find out more about the beetles. Sananda was there when I arrived. We greeted one another with our secret hand shake, like a couple of school children in a den. We sat in a circle and a holographic telescope type piece of apparatus came from above and settled in the middle of the circle. We all looked into the eye piece, like you would in a submarine. The whole planet was covered with these things, beetles everywhere, and swarms of them. The telescope disappeared and we placed a net around Mother Earth and cleaned the insects away. Abba informed me that the healing centre I had my eye on was still up for sale, and that I could use it as offices and a clinic; if I wanted to buy it with my fortune. I told him I would think about it and made my way back.

The mobile had bleeped while I was in the bath, it was a friend asking me if I though debt was related to past lives. I replied saying that it could be a few different things. The first being past life vows of poverty. The second could be self worth issues causing receiving to be difficult. Next, I mentioned fear of lack which can cause a wall to form around you, blocking your abundance. There were many others, but the one that jumped out at me was the first vow. Then I realised that this was a message. I sat on my bed and called Archangel Michael and the angels of purification. He said I needed to transmute old vows made by me as they were blocking my abundance. I asked the angels to gather up these vows, and watched as they placed them into a beautiful white flame to purify them.

"Well done, you're a winner!" said Michael.

I think he was referring to the lottery - I hope he was any way. The fear was gone, the self confidence issues were gone, and now the old vows were gone; so hopefully the money has a clear pathway to me and I can get on with making my dreams come true.

About an hour later I found a letter on the floor by the front door. It said in big bold letters 'DIRECTOR' on it. I knew it was a message to go and see the Divine Director; I had another initiation to receive. I said to myself, I'll journey later and instantly there was a text message from my son, he wanted me to pick him up earlier from college. This meant that the Divine Director wanted to see me now. I didn't have time to have another bath, so I just lay down on my bed and journeyed with Michael to the retreat.

My new Calibration was 2350 and a fourth diamond was placed in the star on my chest. We had a quick chat and I made my way back. I sat in my lounge staring out of the windows at the trees. Lord Thoth came into my mind. I closed my eyes and I could see him, but he was trapped inside a crystal ball just like I was last week. Without hesitation, I pulled out my sword and cut him free. Archangel Michael was standing beside me. When I asked him why he didn't release Thoth, he told me that it was important that I did it myself. Why, I have no idea!

36. 15th Oct 2008 – My Dad's Message

After my Tai Chi class last night I decided I needed to speak to Abba, so I ran myself a bath and made my way to the white room. He sat me down and talked to me about the lottery win I was due, asking me if I was sure that I could handle that amount of money. I told him I was fine with it and gave him a big hug. As he held me I started to cry.

"You miss your father, child, don't you" he said

"I do, I wish he was around to see my achievements"

"Let's go into the garden, I have something I think you might like to see."

We made our way along the white corridor and into the garden where we both sat on a white marble bench. He told me that my father saw my achievements, as spirit can see the future, and that he had left me a recorded message, a holographic message. I asked if I could see it and the hologram appeared before us. My dad was there smiling and telling me that he knew I was a little Goddess when I was born; he was proud of my achievements and would see me at the party when we would all be reunited in the future. I cried like a baby, Abba had his arm around me and suddenly I felt like the child that would sit cuddled up on the couch with my dad, watching an old cowboy movie with John Wayne and Maureen O'Hara in it. This was such a special memory, for a few minutes I felt like I had my dad back. I thanked Abba and we sat quietly in the garden for a while. I slept well last night, more content about life for a change, no need to achieve, I could just BE.

This morning I did a really good clearing on myself and removed old belief systems which were holding me back. I was always being pulled up for giving too much, I helped my friends and students instead of letting them make mistakes, like I did, and still was. The belief system looked like a large turnip shaped energy in the net. I was up to 2362. Abba said that I needed to get up to 2500 by the 30th October. The tears always helped as old grief and pain were released from my body - they are toxic emotions after all.

I noticed that there was a black car parked by the side of my house and I felt something was hanging around. I pulled a net through my home and grounds and sure enough there was a lively ET standing outside. He struggled a bit in the net but soon calmed down.

On the way back from picking my son up from college I noticed a sign, it said 'fresh link'. This always meant that I was to get a new Spiritual Guide, and I was excited to find out who it was. When we got home, I went for a lie down and tuned in. Michael took me to the white room and I sat down.

"Who's my new Guide, Father?" I asked.

"Faith" he said, and the brightest angel I could imagine walked towards me. It was Faith; we had met before, last week in fact. I said hello to her and she embraced me. I was infused with her energy and now calibrated at 2376 as a result. Abba told me that she would help me restore people's faith when I spoke to them.

My friend and I were planning an evening where we would talk to people about self healing and global healing awareness. She would give messages to the audience, as she was a Spiritual Medium. We were looking forward to it. I felt so lucky to have Faith as my Guide; what an honour. I couldn't wait to tell Michael.

37. 16th Oct 2008 – Half man, half toad

Last night I dreamt about a red room, an empty red room in fact. It felt like it was something to do with the medium night I was arranging. When I got up this morning, I decided I needed to speak to Abba to find

74

out what it meant. I soon realised it was telling me about excess base energy. I cleared the room we would be working in, then settled down into my morning meditation. I started with fear and doubt, the net was half full of fine dust, it was greyish in colour.

Then I cleared toxins, pollution and ectoplasm because I had been writing a lot recently. The net had a large shape in it, longer than me; it looked like a giant mutated candle. Dirty ectoplasm came to mind. Once I felt clear, I asked Abba and the angels to please fill all of the voids with exactly what I needed. I was instantly cocooned in a clear diamond pod which then separated into individual molecules, and filled the gaps in my body and my aura, forming a shape like an Archangel around me.

Archangel Michael said that Abba wanted to speak to me, and we made our way up to the white room. I looked like Archangel Michael, the same profile from the neck down, sword and all. It was quite bizarre. I went into the white room where Abba was waiting for me, and I sat down on the crystal table. I know he wanted to talk to me about the lottery. I could sense it. Before he had a chance to speak, I asked him why the jackpot this Friday was only eleven million pounds, I had been told I would be given thirty three million. I began to cry, the stress was getting to me and I was convinced I had done something wrong and ruined my dream of becoming a secret millionaire.

"Have I done something wrong, Father?" I asked.

"No child," he replied, and then he began to explain that the previous Friday he and the Karmic Board had an emergency meeting, and another light worker was given the winning ticket, because she was already more advanced in the business side of the mind body and spirit industry. I was to try this week and I would be guided to invest in stocks and shares, to get the total up to over thirty million, over the next year or so. I felt better after he told me what had happened.

At that point Sanada arrived, and we formed a circle to work on Mother Earth. There were lots of ET's in the first net; they looked like half man, half toad and had four eyes. There was a lot of fuss and struggle as they were taken away. Abba popped them into his white rabbit hole, a sort of waste disposal portal, in the corner of the room. They had been responsible for the little beetle like parasites the other day. Once we had cleared the planet, we had time for a quick chat; Sanada was telling me how well I was doing and that I really did look like an Archangel now. My new level was 2401, I asked where he calibrated and he told me that he was using my techniques to raise his own vibration but gave no figure.

We said our goodbyes, and I made my way back home. Once dried and dressed, it was time to take my son to college. We were about a mile away from home when I felt an uncomfortable pressure in my heart, like it had been crushed. I asked Abba what was wrong and immediately spotted a large black van with the hazard warning lights flashing. Something dark had gone into my heart. I dropped my son off and turned around to drive home. A car passed me called a Ford Focus; this was a sign telling me a message was on the way. The next car had a number plate with a 'V' and 'XXL'; this told me an alien, and an extra large one at that. The next car had a number plate with the word CAT on it; this told me that I had a hook in my heart.

As soon as I got home, I lay down and I closed my eyes to see what was going on. I could see a large ET (about 20ft high) and it had me on a chain leash with a cross type hook into my heart chakra.

76

Archangel Michael cut the chain, the Angels placed a net around the docile creature, and I removed the hook. That felt better, I was clear. I must have forgotten to close my chakra when we left earlier. Michael reminded me of my initiation. I went to the chamber and arrived to applause from Council. The Divine Director placed a gold chain around my neck and another diamond in the star on my breastplate. Lady Nada came towards me and curtseyed. It felt wrong. I asked her never to do that to me again and I kissed her hand and bowed before her.

"If it was not for you mentoring me in Dubai, I would not be who I am today. I honour you for your patience and thank you" I said.

"Thank you", she smiled and I was on my way home.

38. 17th Oct 2008 – 100 times more power

Last night I had a dream about people floating around like they were sky diving. The people on the ground were attracting them back down to earth with large magnets. When I woke up I decided it was a message telling me that I needed grounding, so I looked through my box of crystals and found my hematite necklace to ground myself. It was also good for anxiety and fear which I was releasing every day at the moment; old stuff from past lives.

During my morning clearing, I pulled out a net of fear and doubt first; then continued to clear my body of toxins and general pollution I picked up by just stepping outside of my own home. My oracle cards referred to DNA again and I made my way up to the white room. I lay down on the table; the test tube surrounded me and reprogrammed my DNA. Abba said I was being given more Archangel Essence, and

I could actually feel it coming through my body and working its way out of my feet. It looked like fibre optics, white in colour, and forming a shape like the roots of a tree. Abba called Sananda and they stood either side of my legs and removed a key like implant from each knee. This allowed the essence to flow through me, and to ground it. 2464, WOW!

I looked amazing, just like an Archangel. I mentioned to Abba about the oracle card that told me to choose a magic power and it would be programmed into my DNA. I chose super powers to be used to protect the local universe only, and Abba told me to go to see the Pharaoh and it would be done.

First, I had to go to the chambers to receive my initiation. Divine Director placed another diamond in my star on my breastplate, it was the sixth. Michael and I quickly made our way to see the Pharaoh to have my powers increased.

Archangel Michael spoke to the Pharaoh and I was told to sit in the usual place. An egg shaped rock opened, and I was surrounded in a sphere of light. Grids, like lasers, passed through me in various directions and the fine tuning was complete. I gave a diamond to the Pharaoh which he predictably placed in his third eye. We gave thanks, and we left.

"That will give you 100 times more power when you use it, but only for a short time" said Michael.

"I'm only planning on using it in emergencies." I said.
I felt tired, I wanted to get home and have a sleep. My physical body was weak at the moment, I needed to rest. All of these changes had an affect on my physical body, I need to take extra care of myself and eat well.

Tonight I may or may not win the lottery. Part of me thinks it might be a test to see how I react if my numbers don't come up. I ask Michael but he would not comment. I had decided to let go of my dream and see what happens. I can't be attached to a particular outcome, it will cause problems. May God's will be done!

39. 18th Oct 2008 – Not a Winner

I woke up at the usual time this morning feeling very calm, considering I may have won the lottery. I turned on my computer to check my ticket. My suspicions were right, I didn't win. To be honest I wasn't as upset as I thought I would be. I ran myself a bath and went to see Abba. I must have failed my tests; that's why I didn't win. My mistake; giving too much, he did warn me.

Thursday afternoon a friend of mine visited and I just couldn't stop myself, I gave her advice and read her cards. That was it; I gave too much and could not be trusted with £11 million. I thought fair enough, but I was flat broke, in debt and I needed help. I just wanted to earn a decent living. This was all getting to me and I needed a break. I haven't even had any clients this week, and I keep being told to have faith; then this. I just felt like I wanted to go to sleep and hide under the duvet. It was becoming a chore, life I mean, it felt like I was being punished for being too kind, but the truth was I was blocking my abundance by giving too much. I needed to give and take!

My oracle cards said I was to be given another chance, but to be honest I've decided a bank loan might be the answer for now. My fears about not earning enough are holding me back, I'm sure of it.

Later I had another bath and my clearing today was fairly uneventful. I removed toxins as usual and my level rose to 2476. I went up to the white room and Abba was there with Sananda. He asked me to lie on the crystal table. He stood at my feet with Sananda and they removed a kind of looped key from my ankles. These released implants from my legs, hips, spine and shoulders, that looked like rods. I felt like I had a small void running through me, and Abba said not to worry, they would be filled with Goddess energy later.

As I now calibrated at 2502, I was called to the chamber at the retreat for another initiation. Sananda came with me and we talked about the stress the lottery was causing me. He also just advised me to have faith, the same as Abba and Michael. Faith, they all said to have faith, so faith was my best friend. The Divine Director placed my 7th diamond into the star in my chest and gave me another sword; it opened out like a fan and formed a protective shield.

40. 19th Oct 2008 – The Crystal Tablet

Last night I had a dream about an angry man in a wheelchair and a large swimming pool. I realised that it was a message to clear out my anger, as it was disabling me.

Before I had my morning meditation I called Tess to catch up on how life was treating her. She was becoming more and more sensitive to people's energy and like me had become quite reclusive. Just before the end of the phone call her son had given her an Indiana Jones toy and she made a point of mentioning it. It immediately made me think about the Crystal Skulls. I pulled out an oracle card after the call and it was hawk medicine, which meant that I was

80

being sent a message. I needed to go to the Sphinx, so it looked like I had a busy journey ahead.

Once in the bath tub I cleared myself of fear and anger, which brought me up to 2516. Archangel Michael insisted on carrying me to the Sphinx to conserve my energy. Once in the room with the Pharaoh, Michael spoke of Abba's instructions to have my blueprint encoded with Goddess essence. I sat down in the chair as before. The egg shaped rock now looked like a diamond; it opened up and surrounded me in a ball of light. As I looked at the egg, a shape began to form. It looked like a woman's body and it moved towards me as particles of light, and merged into my body. It felt divine, more than divine. A grid running horizontally across me moved down through my body to my feet, expelling old negative ego programs. I felt fantastic, I handed the Pharaoh a diamond, then left.

We needed to go and see the Crystal Skulls and again, Michael insisted on carrying me to save my energy.

Peru was beautiful and sunny. We made our way down the many steps deep into the heart of the Temple, where the Skulls resided. I walked into the centre of the circle of these amazing beings.

"We have a quest for you Serena." The skull spoke in a voice I recognised.

They often called me by my angel name. He continued to explain that a dark Sorcerer in the Middle East was in possession of a crystal tablet which had a formula encoded into it. The code was part of the keys to creation, but in the wrong hands could destroy the whole planet. It was kept in a chest in a locked room, and I was to retrieve it and return it to Abba.

Michael was to guide me on my quest; this quest was part of my journey and involved some risk. I was to take care and to go tomorrow night at 9pm.

41. 20th Oct 2008 – Fusion

I felt like I had more fear in me that needed clearing, also anger. I couldn't stop thinking that somehow Abba had let me down and I was angry with him for my present financial situation. I went to see him after I had cleaned myself but I still was not happy with my lot. I could sense an awkward feeling when I was with him; why couldn't I let go of my disappointment?

My faith had been damaged and I had less than two weeks to go before my first real public speaking event where I was meant to be helping people restore their faith. I needed to sort this problem out and quickly. I could not even look him in the eye. I felt so low about the whole situation. Abba told me to go and sit in the garden for a while. I walked through the doorway out of the white room and made my way over to a marble bench and lay down on it like a lost child. I started to cry. I was annoyed with myself as much as anybody else. I felt warmth pass over me and I looked up to see Faith standing behind me. She wrapped a blanket of her energy around me and I sat up.

I needed her help. She put her arms around me and held me like a mother would hold her baby. Cradled in her glow, I rested for a while just absorbing the light. She told me that Abba was sad that I did not trust he would take care of me, she said he felt my disappointment and I felt really bad. I didn't know what to do to make things better. I asked her to stay with me and help me to gain my faith in Abba and let go of my fears.

Later that day I Michael insisted on carrying me to the white room to save my energy. Abba was sitting chatting to Sananda. I joined them and we all agreed to do a clearing on the planet and then a DNA cleanse on me. The first net we pulled through the planet had about 50,000 ET's in it. That put my total souls collected so far up to 1,120,000. The second net was to collect stagnant male energy and it was like thick grey soup; the third was fear and avarice which looked like coal in the net and black rocks.

Abba asked me to lie on the healing table and the test tube formed around me. Before we started I asked Abba if he could remove my fear receptors, he just smiled at me. Once the light had reprogrammed me with the new essence Sananda removed a large key from my earth star chakra below my feet. It would allow my new goddess essence to ground into it and released two large chains which seemed to tie my chakra to the centre of the planet. It seemed that once this higher energy was connected to my earth star, the chains were no longer needed. My new level was 2640, I could hardly believe it.

I climbed down from the table and asked Abba if I still needed to carry out my quest. He said the choice was mine, I decided I wanted to do it now as previously agreed with the skulls. Earlier today my son was telling me about his new computer game and how the warriors in it joined their powers together to make them temporarily stronger. He said that they called it fusion. I spoke to Michael about it and he agreed that we should do it before we went on our mission. We walked toward one another and merged as one being then passed through the back of one another, our powers fused together.

"Have I weakened you Michael?" I asked.

"No, I have all of your strengths and none of your weaknesses." he replied.

We both had an energy buzzing around us like silver dust, we shone like stars. It was time to go. Cloaking ourselves we became invisible to all except one another and we made our way out of the room and through a long tunnel made of light, it was the worm hole I'd been through before. Next thing I know we were out of the end and into the super universe where I had met Michael's friend Osirus and the doughnut worm. I looked towards our entrance back into the local universe and was amazed to see hundreds of star gates. Which one was the right one? I had no idea, luckily Michael did and we flew through another worm hole at light speed. Within seconds we were back on Earth somewhere in the Middle East. As we drew closer to our destination I asked Abba to make the outside of our transport portal soundproof and invisible to the dark energies guarding the treasure chest. Then I was there, in the room, it was sand stone and full of gold and gemstones. I looked around and could see the chest. I pulled out my sword and gently sliced through the lock and opened the lid.

There was a crystal tablet about 10 x 4 inches and 1 inch thick. To my surprise it had a golden key inside with symbols marked along the shaft. I grabbed it and handled it to my companion. He placed it inside his breastplate. I closed the chest and we were gone back through the star gates and to the white room to see Abba. Michael gave the key to me and I handed it to Father, he placed it safely into his heart chakra.

"Well done, my child". He said.

I placed my arms around him and told him I was sorry about the last few days. My faith was back, my quest completed. I came home a happy light worker with peace of mind. 10pm – time for supper.

42. 21st Oct 2008 – The 8th Diamond

Today I asked my physical body what it needed and was told to take a trip to the crystal city because my pancreas was only functioning at 75% efficiency but apart from that I was in pretty good shape. My mental body asked me to read a bit more fiction and relax a bit more. My emotional body was okay but needed a hug, just a little bit of nurturing was called for. My spiritual body was floating, fantastically balanced and very happy indeed, possibly a bit more grounding was necessary but that was all. I asked to speak to my higher self and soon realised that it was my God self I could see. Golden white light radiated from a beautiful image of a face floating before me. My God self told me to keep writing my books and not to worry about money. Easier said than done but I could only do my best. I just needed to keep removing the fear and replacing it with faith and I'd be fine.

I needed to go with Andrew to get my pancreas balanced. We made our way to the crystal city and I lay in the casket full of white light which was absorbed into my pancreas. After that I said goodbye to Andrew and went with Michael for my initiation. The Divine director placed the last diamond in the star on my breastplate no. 8 and the star grew larger and surrounded my whole body then became part of my essence. I was informed that this guaranteed me protection, it was the God star and I could now safely travel through the Super Universe and Havona Worlds without Archangel Michael. I would be untouchable. It sounded good to me, I said thank you and left the chamber to a round of applause from the Council.

43. 22nd Oct 2008 – The Key to Creation

Once clear at 2652 I made my way to the retreat and into the chamber where the council sat calmly as usual. I walked over to the Divine director and he placed a diamond in the wrist plate on my left hand. I gave thanks and because I was short on time I got straight home. It was 10pm and I needed to eat.

As we left Michael was skipping around me like a child.

"What is wrong with you Michael?" I asked.

"I am so happy for you, you are about to receive the rewards of your labour. I am looking forward to seeing your worries removed, to seeing you smile" he replied.

"Oh, that's what it is", I said.

I realised what was going on, he wanted me to have fun and rejoice too but I still had work to do before I was ready to play. We made our way down the long stairwell into the heart of the Temple and composed ourselves. We entered the room, Michael held back and I walked into the centre of the circle. As soon as I got there, four rays of light formed from four of the crystal skulls and formed a holographic box of light just in front of me. Inside the box was a golden key about 8 inches long. It looked like the key in the crystal tablet I gave to Abba a few days ago.

"This is the key of creation, it is yours. You have proven yourself worthy of ownership and put the needs of many before your own. You may now grant your wish. Put your hand into the box".

I gently lifted my right arm and placed my hand into the box of light. The key moved into my wrist and became invisible.

"Where is it?" I asked.

"It is part of your Goddess essence, place your wrist across your heart and make your wish" I was instructed by the skull.

I put my arm across my chest and the key appeared and joined with the orb Sananda had given me at my planetary Princess initiation. I made my wish, the key retuned into my wrist and it was done. The empty box vanished. Sha Na Ra came over to me and hugged me. I was a bit overwhelmed to be honest, for the first time. This key gave me the power to create whatever I wished, what was I going to do with it, what do I need to create. Questions ran through my mind, the skull hearing them all stopped me and said.

"Worry not child, you will be guided when the key needs to be used".

"Thank God for that", I thought.

I thanked the skulls, bid them farewell and left the room. I was a bit shocked really. Once outside my shock turned to excitement. I was holding Michaels hands and jumping up and down. I was worthy; at last, I was worthy. Michael was smiling like a Cheshire cat. At that point I realised that over the last few weeks while I was struggling to clear my old fears, he had been with me every day and he could feel my pain. At points I was so low I felt like giving up my spiritual work altogether but he never left me. I could feel the love he had and that's why he was so happy for me now, the worst was behind me and the road ahead looked clear and straight.

We were soon back inside a worm hole and in the super universe again.

"Would you like to face one more fear before we head back?" he said and of course I said yes.

I closed my eyes and I was standing on top of the Empire State building looking down onto the streets below, the cars were like ants scurrying around.

"Jump." I heard a voice say. "Jump."

I glanced down and the busy streets turned to a deep blackness, nothing but black. I'd seen this before. This was the void, the empty unknown between now and the future, a space that must be conquered in order to move forward.

Without hesitation I jumped, my face feeling the wind, it was cool, my heart raced. I was falling face first into the void of creation at high speed. Suddenly I began to slow down and I glanced over my shoulder to see a vision of five little cherubs holding my arms and legs. They had me, they saved me from what I will never know but I was meant to be with them. I know that much. The darkness turned into another worm hole full of different coloured lines of light. It curved and dropped until we were spat out into Abba's garden. They gently placed me on a patch of white lawn next to a small pond of crystal white fish. Full of joy and giggles, they tidied me up a little and pointed toward the pond.

I walked closer and sat down on the edge. The fish swam nearer and I placed my hand in the water slowly so as not to frighten them. One by one they came to my hand and brushed up against me, they were pure bliss, I could feel a different vibration for each one of them as if they had names that were musical notes.

Once of the cherubs clapped her hands twice and the fish swam down out of sight. She pointed at the water and I could see myself clear as day. I was being handed a cheque and by the look on my face it was a substantial amount of money. Was this a vision of me receiving the lottery win, it must be, why else would they show me this? This vision faded and the fish were back. The cherubs lifted me up and took me to a tree, the tree was large and wide, it looked like my willow tree back home.

They sat me down in a chair made of rope which hung underneath the beautiful tree and I waited for something to happen. Instantly the wise old tree said hello to me and welcomed me to the garden. He continued…

"You are an important leader Serena. From your place of power, you need be constantly aware of keeping peace, you must always tell the truth, know it and live it, and you will lead by example. The mountain lion will help you to learn how to balance intention, power, strength and grace, to balance your mind, body and spirit and to lead without insisting that others follow. Wolf will help you teach as you follow your destiny and clear your mind of negative thoughts. But most of all be integral, jaguar will help you with this. His essence is integrity and impeccability; he removes the unclean aspects of human behaviour. Serve mankind with compassion and be your personal best at all times. Control your ego and do not be influenced by any other than Source."

"Thank you for your guidance, I will do my best."

I closed my eyes for a second and when I opened them I was home.

44. 24th Oct 2008 – The Gregorian Warriors

Michael said Abba wanted to speak to us. He said it was important to keep my flying down to a minimum as to conserve my energy, that's why he was carrying me. When we got to the landing at the top, all I could see was a pair of hairy knees. I looked up and could see Thoth.

"Lord Thoth, greetings." I said.

He looked down, turned around and sat on the floor next to me, my eyes in line with his huge chest and breast plate.

"Greetings Serena. We got off to a bad start the first time we met, I showed you little mercy but I have been watching you and I am impressed, you have done well."

"Thank you. I am only human, well more or less; why are we called here today?"

"You will soon see, come child, let us go inside".

We walked into the room, I sat down next to Sananda and Michael stood next to Thoth. Abba was standing beside the crystal healing table, he spoke in a solemn voice and informed us that Sirius had been invaded by an army from sector 14 of our local universe. Blackthorn, the leader of the Gregorian Warriors had kidnapped the Syrian Emperor and was holding him captive, demanding a ransom.

At this point I could see Blackthorn in my mind's eye, he had the body of a man but he had large antlers like a stag, deadly weapons he was not afraid to use.

"What does he ask for?" said Sananda. At this point I expected something like, the head of John the Baptist or similar, and guess what? I wasn't far off.

"The right hand of Janine of Warwick" said Abba.

All eyes were on me, news travels fast, he wanted the key, which was in my wrist. To my surprise I felt quite calm about the situation.

"What do you want us to do father?" I asked.

"Tonight at 9pm, you and Michael will go to Blackthorn and on my behalf request he leaves Sirius peacefully of his own free will. If he refuses, the band of mercy will quickly net the whole planet and pull him and his warriors out of Sirius and they will be placed into universal lockdown until further notice. He has weapons and he is dangerous, use your sword as a shield and fuse your powers before you leave".

I looked at Michael and he nodded his head slightly as if to say, fine by me.

"OK father, we will do what we can".

"Remember, talk first, then the code word firefly will release the nets should he not surrender his position". As we made our way down the steps I asked him why nobody was bothered when Satan was around listening to us.

"He is a lost soul, my brother as much as you are. We do not judge fear or despise him, as with all of creation, he has his part to play. Do you understand?"

"Yes, I do" I replied.

About 2 hours later at 2pm I received a message to go to the Retreat. I lay down and tuned in, we were soon there and once we had greeted the Council I made my way over to the Divine director. He congratulated me and placed the 10th diamond in my left wrist plate. I thanked him and we were gone.

At 8.30pm I ran myself a warm bath, lit my candles and called for Archangel Michael and his divine helpers. I asked my higher self to shape shift me into a safe shape and was told I needed to be me, just the way I was. I looked very much like Archangel Michael except for my long red hair. I could see Michael clearly and we made our way up to the white room where Abba, Sananda and Thoth were waiting for us.

We sat down and Abba instructed us that we were to offer Blackthorn the chance to surrender and not to take any chances. Thoth handed me a clear orb of energy, it was a pure peace. He told me to give it to Blackthorn and explain to him that Abba promises an infinite supply if he chooses to leave peacefully and take the path of light. I took the orb and placed it in my heart for safe keeping.

"Remember; the code is firefly" said Abba.

We stood up and prepared for fusion, Michael walked into my body and out of the back. We were powered up, a force to be reckoned with. We left via the doorway which led to the garden; only this time it took us into a wormhole and out into the universe. We flew toward Sirius and landed in a forest, it was dense, the grass was up to my chest. I could hear an alarm outside my bathroom window, something was wrong. I felt the ground beneath me disappear and I was falling down a hole, I reached out and grabbed Michael's foot. We hit the ground hard. Even though we were invisible, there were two guards who heard the noise and ran towards us. I pulled out my sword which formed a domed shield around us.

"Tell your master, we seek his council", said Michael.

The two guards looked stunned and passed the message to their leader via a primitive system of communication.

"Go along that corridor, he is waiting", one of them pointed to a tunnel through the rocks.

As we walked along it my sword formed a wall to protect us from the guards. We got to a door and Michael knocked twice. Another guard opened the door and we entered a sparsely filled room; Blackthorn looked angry. We stood before him and Michael spoke.

"The father has asked us to come. He requests you to surrender and return to sector A"

"Why should I surrender, who is this?" he pointed at me.

"They call me Janine of Warwick" I replied.

"Janine of Warwick, I want your hand. You stand before me, what is to stop me taking it from you?" he growled.

"Abba asked me to give you this". I pulled out the orb and handed it to Blackthorn.

"Michael, I don't like his energy, he is determined" I said to Michael using our telepathic line.

"Hold back Janine, wait." said Michael.

As Blackthorn examined the orb I told him that Abba promised more of the same if he was to lay down his arms and return to his own planet but it fell on deaf ears.

"He's going to attack me, I can feel it," I said.

"Okay, go for it", said Michael.

"Firefly, firefly", I yelled.

A huge net engulfed the room and he was captured. The band of mercy netted the whole planet and all 4000 of his warriors were taken away. He glanced at us through the net, I repeated, Peace be with you until he was gone.

"Phew! I'm glad that's over Michael".

"Well done Janine, you kept calm, well done".

We left the room and made our way back down the dark corridor. Michael opened a door and we were travelling along another worm hole, in minutes we were back in the white room.

Thoth and Sananda stood up and cheered as we entered, Abba smiled his loving smile.

"Well done", he said, he opened a box and inside were two stars, six pointed like sheriffs badges but elongated. He placed one on my breast plate and one on Michaels.

"This is to mark your courage, you are brave warriors", said Abba, "Peace be with you".

"Peace be with you father", we replied.

We left the room and the crystal staircase turned into a large slide, we both jumped on the slide and flew down like a couple of excited school boys. What a fantastic day!

45. 26th Oct 2008 – My lips are sealed

Michael said that Abba wanted to see me, he carried me up to the white room and when I went inside I could see Thoth and Sananda sitting with Abba.

"You called for me father", I said.

"We just wanted to make sure you are aware that your quests and tasks such as the crystal tablet and Sirius are kept secret. You are not to discuss them with your friends", said Abba.

"Ok, fine, my lips are sealed."

"These tasks are for level 4 Havana world candidates only. You do realise that you are one of those candidates?"

Only yesterday I read about being given tasks to do to work your way through the Havona Worlds.

"Yes father, how am I doing?"

"You are doing well my child",

Lord Thoth and Sananda looked at me and nodded with approval.

"It is important that you rest, be balanced, put a little time each day aside to write your book. The rest of the time, take it easy, you need to conserve your energy for the path ahead".

"I will do my best", I said. "Thank you".

I bid them all farewell and made my way home with Michael by my side as always.

46. 27th Oct 2008 – 2 Diamonds

Michael and I were at the retreat today. We entered the chamber where the Council sat as always. I wanted to get home to bed so I didn't take a seat. I walked straight over to the Divine Director and held my right arm up. He placed the 2nd diamond in the wrist plate and it got larger and expanded to nearly my elbow. Both wrist plates had 2 diamonds now, only the shins left. 4 more diamonds and I would receive my Goddess initiation; I hope they know what they're doing. I said thank you nodded my head to Council and we were on our way back.

47. 28th Oct 2008 – Ryan the Bold

The first thing I did today was text Tess and let her know about the collar. She was as enlightened as me and didn't even question it. She said she would check herself over as soon as she could.

It was midday by the time I did my morning clearing with one thing and another. I had a twitch in my ear, I asked my higher self what it was and was informed that it was an old implant that was blocking some of my clairvoyant abilities. It looked like three or four pieces of a jigsaw puzzle welded together but not evenly and flat like a jigsaw. The pieces were stepped and the edges were square not round. It also had two wires which ran down my spine and attached to my heart chakra. I removed the whole thing easily with the help of my angels.

Once it was out I could see a key, a big old fashioned type. Keys always meant soul retrieval was imminent. Soon I could see a man in a prison cell; he was sitting down with his head in his hands. I asked the man why he was there and he said he had been locked up for killing his wife. She fell in the kitchen and the knife she was cutting vegetables with stabbed her as she hit the ground. By the time help arrived he was cradling her and they thought he had murdered her. He was waiting to be tried for murder.

As with all lost souls I asked him what his name was and what he wanted to happen. He said William and that he just wanted someone to believe him. I told him that I believed him and if he came with me, he would be free of his torment. He stood up and I opened my heart chakra allowing him to come home; it was me nearly 500 years ago. As soon as he was back I could see angels around him and he was at peace. I had another soul fragment back in place.

Michael called me and said Abba wanted to speak to me. We went up to the white room and inside was a man I sort of recognised but I wasn't sure.

"This is Ryan the Bold," said Abba.

"Pleased to meet you again Ryan," I held out my hand and we shook, the secret hand shake I only shared with Michael and Sananda.

"Ryan will help you teach the elementals; he will come to your talks and workshops. He will be with you and Faith on Thursday."

"Excellent," I said "Will there be anything else Father?"

"No child, go to the mountain with Michael before you return."

I said goodbye and Michael and I made our way to Mount Shasta. Michael had never been here with me before I usually came with white bear. I asked the mountain if he had a message for me and he said,
"You are saintly in your demeanour; your debut appearance on Thursday will go well and is the first of many. You are much loved and blessed by the Father and the wise ones. Go in Peace."

There wasn't much to say really. As Michael and I made our way back he told me that I might be made a saint. I have noticed the word around me over the last few days but I thought nothing of it.

"Don't be silly Michael, you're pulling my leg".

"I'm not Janine, it is possible," he said.

I just found that a bit too much to take on board. A saint indeed; moments later I was home.

48. 29th Oct 2008 - The Crystal Ki Foundation

I sat down next to Willow and he told me I had to clear something from my memory, an old fear relating to money. It was blocking my abundance. When I looked I could see a bubble around me, a bubble of fear, it was keeping me trapped. I pulled a net down through myself and the old image began to appear. I could see myself, it was about 12th Century. Armed guards entered my house, killed my wife and children as they slept and left me dying on the floor. My crime, I could not pay my taxes. The whole scenario was removed from my body and light filled the gaps.

This afternoon I popped out in my car to go to the shops, it was lunch time and the roads were particularly busy. I had a message from a friend saying she had sold four more tickets for the medium event my friend and I were organising tomorrow night. We were hoping to get 30 or 40 people together and we were both excited about it. After the message I said thank you to Abba for guiding more people to us.
I was driving slowly and looked to the side of the road to see a woman wearing a sweat shirt with the words "HAPPY TO HELP". Who buys a top with happy to help on it? I knew it was another little miracle, Abba's response, I chuckled to myself.

Later I ran myself a bath and settled in. I was taken by Michael up to the white room where Abba and Sananda were waiting for me. Abba said that he wanted to reprogram my DNA to the next level 2936 but first him and Sananda would remove the implants either side of my head to improve my clairaudience.

I lay on the crystal table, they stood either side of my head, four screws held a mechanical housing in position tight to my skull. They removed the screws and the housing slid outwards about an inch from my scalp. A small flat metallic disc was removed from the housing and then it was pushed back into position and the screws replaced. The disc must have been the implants. Abba threw them into the rabbit holes, his waste disposal unit. Then the test tube surrounded me and the DNA reprogramming was carried out. It all took less than a couple of minutes. I sat up and thanked them both. Abba said it was time to go to the retreat to sign my new contract. I was excited but apprehensive at the same time. Sananda, Michael and I all left the room via the magical back door and

99

we were soon at the retreat walking along the cold stone corridor to the main chamber. Once inside they sat down, Michael in his own seat and Sananda in mine. I walked straight across to the Divine Director and he placed a diamond into my left shin plate.

"Your new contract involves three years as a spiritual teacher, travelling the world promoting enlightenment. You will be founder of the Crystal Ki foundation to help those in need. After the three years you will remove yourself from the public eye and retreat for the next 12 months in preparation for the cosmic event on 21st Dec 2012. Do you accept this?"

"How am I to fund this work?"

"You will be placed in charge of a trust funded by lottery money" he replied.

I accepted it and Lady Nada came toward me with a small box that looked like a treasure chest. She opened it and I could see a cheque inside. She asked me to sign it in order to endorse it and I did as she requested. I thanked them both and made my way back to the white room with Sananda and Michael. Abba was there waiting for us, I told him I was happy with the new contract and in the blink of an eye I was home.

49. 30th Oct 2008 – My Debut Event

Tonight was my debut appearance as a spiritual teacher. I had a terrible dream last night. I dreamt that someone was trying to possess me. The feeling was so powerful I woke up and it was true. A large being was trying to force its way into my body via my left side. I quickly called on Archangel Michael and he pulled it out in a net, the being was alien, about 7ft tall and gremlin like in appearance. I had seen this type of

ET before, they could be quite nasty. Michael wrapped his wings around me and I soon drifted back off to sleep.

I went with Michael to see Abba, I asked what he wanted me to focus on this evening at the event and he said global healing awareness. This meant that I needed to explain to the group that we are the ones that will make the necessary changes to our planet because we create the world we live in. Our every thought word and deed make a difference because of the energy they produce. That energy reflects in to the world around us, the good, the bad and the ugly; therefore we are the ones who need to create the positive changes. Michael took me to the mountain and we sat on a ledge, I asked the mountain for a message of wisdom. He told me that there would be much wisdom and love in the room tonight and that no darkness would gain entry. I needed to hear that, it put my mind at rest.

All of the tickets were sold, I was so pleased. There were rows and rows of angels, spirits and high priests around the room. As the evening began, I stood up in front of about forty people and bang, something hit me in the chest and throat. I was virtually rendered speechless and had tears in my eyes. The crowd though I was having an attack of nerves but I wasn't, it was a feeling I had not known before. A mixture of love and sadness rushed through my heart and out of my throat. I talked about global healing awareness for twenty minutes or so and we had a short break before my friend came on the floor to deliver messages from spirit. A very wise old soul spoke first and told everyone that they were all light workers, very special and much loved. Some of the audience looked a bit surprised. I don't think that they had seen any one channelling before; it must have seemed a little strange at first.

A little girl who had been hanging around my friend all day was there with Jesus. She told us that when children die, they are brought to Jesus and he makes them better. She said she had a white puppy and that they played and went to bed just like before. She said that they missed their mummies and daddies sometimes but Jesus always cheered them up and he would play games with them. She said she had two little pockets on the front of her dress to put things in and we all smiled. All in all the evening went well and I looked forward to the next chance to speak to a group.

50. 1st Nov 2008 – Goddess of the Light Warriors

I made a point of not checking my lottery ticket last night because either way I wouldn't be able to sleep afterwards. I would be too excited to sleep if I won, and too upset to sleep if I didn't. I knew I had to keep it a secret; that was for sure. On the way to buy the ticket, I saw a number plate with LYNX on it. Lynx energy is about secrets, according to my oracle cards. That sign alone convinced me I had to win this weekend, and the fact that it was a £33m roll-over; just the right amount.

I turned on my computer and googled Euro millions results. Once onto the web site I had a feeling of doubt come over me, and when I checked the winning numbers for last night I knew why. Not one; not one single number. I expected to be really upset but I took the bad news well.

I ran myself a hot bath, lit my meditation candle and sprinkled the water with sea salt crystals. As I cleared myself of the usual stuff, toxins and pollutants mainly, I started to think about the lottery. Last night felt so right, the feeling I had when I bought the ticket, the lynx sign, it all felt like it was really going to happen this time. What did I do to block it, I wonder? I decided to go and see Abba. When I got there Sananda was chatting with him, as was pretty much the norm. Abba told me he pulled back on my numbers coming up because I told Tess about my calibration reaching 3000. "What?" I was overcome with a rush of negative emotions. How could he judge me so harshly? She was going to do a treatment on me next week anyway; she would be able to tell my calibration as soon as she touched me.

At that moment my Fairy Godmother turned up. She asked me to make a wish.

"What's the point?" I was so upset.
.
"Make a wish", she insisted.

"I wish I wasn't in debt and had enough money to pay my bills" I grumbled. "It won't come true because I don't believe any more. My faith has just been destroyed. "You have made a wrong decision Father, I know I have no right to speak to you this way, but you have made a mistake".

"Your wish is granted", said Fairy Godmother.

"It's a waste of time!" I said to her, sobbing like a child.

She looked at Abba. I was distraught, not about the money; I couldn't care less about that. It was about being judged so harshly. I felt like my father had told me it was Christmas tomorrow and then cancelled it because I'd forgotten to clean my teeth, or something as equally pathetic. Fairy Godmother looked at me with such sympathy. I knew she could feel my pain.

103

"We need to go to the chamber for your Coronation, Serena" said Abba.

"If I'm not good enough to be placed in trust of £33 million pounds, I'm not good enough to be crowned." I walked out of the room, determined to boycott my coronation, completely.

The crystal steps became a slide, like you would find in a water park. I jumped on and landed on the ground with a bang. Archangel Michael followed and sat down beside me. I was sobbing uncontrollably by this time, I couldn't believe it.

"Janine, think about what you are about to throw away. No human has ever been crowned whilst still in human form. Abba is upset.

"He has just ripped my heart out, Michael. Do you think he made the right decision? Do you?

"No, I do not and I am not alone, but the decision has been made and you still have another chance to win the money"

"I don't care, I don't want another chance, he's pushed me too far Michael. I can't take any more. I can't remember ever feeling this way before. I'm angry with Abba and I don't trust him. It's killing me to even say it, but that's the way I feel." I just sobbed and my whole body was shaking. I couldn't understand why I was in such a state. Michael held me in his arms and after a few minutes I calmed down.

"Come to your Coronation Janine, please."

It's not easy to refuse Michael with his charm and those amazing blue eyes, so I gave in.

"Okay, I'll come." I pulled myself together and Michael carried me back up to the white room

"It'll be all right, sweetheart," said Fairy Godmother. I looked at her beautiful warm face with tears in my eyes, but "It won't", was running through my mind.

Abba asked me to lie down on the table which I did, trying to avoid eye contact with him. I felt like a child in a mood and had no control over it. He opened my brow chakra pulled out some sort of silver metal contraption and removed a small round metal disc from the centre of my skull, behind my third eye. It must have been another implant. He replaced the housing and we were all on our way. I was calibrating at 3002.

We all left the white room, via the garden door, and made our way to the retreat. When we entered the room the Councillors, and many other beings I didn't recognise, stood up and applauded. Sananda and Michael sat down and Abba guided me to a seat in the centre of the chamber. It was more like a throne than a chair. The Divine Director came over with a beautiful gold crown covered in various coloured precious gems, on top of a royal blue cushion. Abba picked up the crown and placed it on my head.

"Goddess Serena, Goddess of the Light Warriors." said the Divine Director.

Then a large gold breastplate, also covered in gems, was placed on my chest and stomach area. It wrapped itself around my sides and back, and moulded itself perfectly to the shape of my upper torso, as if it was alive. Golden jewelled slippers were placed on my feet and the Coronation was complete. I was given an orb and a sceptre and we all made our way to another room where a feast was prepared in celebration of the event.

I sat to the left of Abba, at the head of the table, and Michael sat to his right next to Sananda. There was food and everybody was laughing and joking. It was a real party atmosphere. Not being one for parties these days, I turned to Abba and asked him if I could be excused. "This celebration is in your honour; stay a little longer", he said gently. I just smiled and nodded.

There were Cherubs playing beautiful music on harps and trumpets. The far end of the room was so bright; I could hardly look at it. The celestial beings shone like beacons, the glow was amazing. Michael and Sananda were engrossed in conversation and everyone was enjoying the gathering. I felt out of place, it was all a bit much for me. I never really did like parties, unless I'd been drinking alcohol, and those days were long gone. I turned to Abba and asked if I could be excused again and this time he said "Go in peace, my child, if you must".
"I must", I replied. But before I left, he stood up, clapped his hands and the room went silent; all eyes were on us.

"Goddess Serena, our honoured guest must leave us now," he said, and the whole room began to clap as I made my way towards the door. Michael stood up to come with me but I told him to stay with Sananda, I could find my own way back. In no time, I was home; a Goddess; a secret, a broken soul.

I felt really low and by the time I got to bed I was heavy. My mood was attracting dense energy to me. I pulled a net through me and it was full of blackness, a huge dark cloud. I lay in bed crying. I thought I heard Abba saying that he was sorry and that he did not intend the decision to cause me so much pain. I replied, "This should have been the most important day of my life so far Father, and your decision ruined it. I feel like a broken heart; the day can never be lived again, the damage that had been done may not be repairable. I despise myself for the way I feel toward you, but I can't stop it. I'm sorry, but I think you may have pushed me too far this time. Please leave me alone". His image disappeared and I cried like a child into the early hours of the morning.

51. 3rd Nov 2008 – The Overdraft

I was a little lighter when I got up today. I ran myself a hot bath and settled into clearing the dark cloud away. My aura was a real mess, full of rubbish. My upper back felt a bit better, but it was still painful. I asked Michael to help me clear it, my heart was painful. This was old stuff coming out, and as the net passed through me it pulled out half a dozen or so, what looked like huge swords, sticking vertically down my spine. Once they were out, the pain ceased.

"That was the reason" said Michael

"What do you mean?"

"That pain and the swords represented every time someone or something had broken you; as you describe it, trauma's and serious heart breaks. This whole incident with you and Abba has brought this energy up to be released. You had to feel it to release it. Do you understand now?"

"Yes, I understand, but it was dreadful. I don't want to go through that feeling again"

"Your calibration has gone up to 3042 because of it".

I began to cry again, it was a relief more than anything. I lay in the bath for a good 20 minutes crying my eyes out.

"3056" said Michael. "Abba wants to see you."

He carried me up to the white room and we both went inside. I still felt a little uncomfortable with Abba. I felt guilty for being angry at him.

"Sit down" he said. "Do you understand why I stopped the lottery win now, my child? It was not just because of talking to Tess. It was to help you release that block in the back of your heart"

"I do, but I'm still feeling very delicate" "I want you to climb the next mountain. At 3500 you will be made a Saint. You have enlightened almost 1.2 million souls, another 300,000 and you can be made a Saint. What do you say?"

"You must be joking, you must be. I'm not fit to wear this Goddess crown never mind to be made a Saint. I couldn't take any more of the way I've felt over the weekend. It's too hard I'm not ready for that, I'm not pure enough"

"You are, and you will be" said Abba

"I need time to think about this, and I would like my money problems put to bed, I am having sleepless nights about my overdraft. My mind needs to be clear to take this on" I stood up to walk away.

"You need to go for your initiation" said Michael.

I started to cry again, "Not today Michael, not now". I left the room and started to walk down the crystal steps. I heard Abba say to Michael, "Comfort the girl,

108

I will send her some help". Michael sat with me at the bottom of the steps, and he placed his arm around me.

"He's God Michael; he can sort this overdraft out for me, surely." My mind thought about the key in my wrist. I hold the key to creation in my essence, and I'm broke, it's ridiculous.

"He will, do not worry", said Michael. The next thing I knew, I was home and the water was cold. I dried myself and went into my bedroom to find some clothes. As I pulled my sweat pants on, I felt a brief pain in my right wrist, the key. It was where the key was. A voice in my head told me to lie on my bed, place the key to my heart and say "May God's will be done".

As I did this I could see the key move, it went into the gold orb in my heart given to me by Sananda, and turned in a lock. The screen in my minds eye showed me my bank statement, -£4,236.48. The minus turned to a plus sign, and all of the figures started to shuffle around, rearranging themselves to +£4236.48. I got the feeling that my account had been credited by God. As quickly as it began, it ended. I decided to cut ties with money, and pulled a net through me to release the associated fears and I felt much better.

52. 4th Nov 2008 – Into the Void

I spent the first couple of hours this morning writing my diary. It was midday by the time I got around to my morning clearing and meditation. The bath water was a bit hot and I turned pink all over as soon as I lay down. I pulled some nets through me, and cleared a lot of worry and anxiety that had been haunting me over the last few days. It was like a huge black fog or cloud as it was removed in the net,

109

the relief was instant, I felt much lighter straight away. All of the stress of the last few days had really got to me. I decided to pull a net through me to remove any negative memories associated with the weekend.

As I focused, I found myself looking down the inside of a large tree trunk; it was just a black hole. I realised this was an opportunity to pass through the void, I'd done it before. I crawled along the inside of the dark tree trunk. When I reached the end, all there was before me was pitch black emptiness in every conceivable direction. The pit of darkness called me and I jumped, tingling with excitement, into the blackness. As I fell into the abyss, at what felt like 1000 miles an hour, I could feel my fears leaving me. I felt peace, freedom, contentment and a million other beautiful feelings in every cell in my body. Somehow, I just knew that everything was going to be all right. At that moment, five little Cherubs took hold of my limbs and body, and I slowed down to a floating pace. They gently lowered me to the ground; the darkness disappeared. As my feet touched the grass, I could see a large lake in a forest enclosure.

The sun was shining and the air was still, silence, apart from the few birds high in the tree tops above me. About 100 yards away across the lake, I could see a doorway into the side of a white cliff. I paddled across the shallow water towards to the door. I opened the door and stepped inside. There was a beautiful neon blue lagoon inside, the roof was made of crystal stalactites of varies shapes and sizes. It was amazing, the water was luminous and at least the size of a football pitch.

"Is it safe?" came into my mind, as I was tempted to dive straight in and experience the delights of the vision before me. All of a sudden, from the water, a huge serpent shot out and swallowed me whole. I managed to get to my feet, and about 10ft away I could see a large golden key; I ran toward it and picked it up. I turned back and ran to the head that had gulped me up like a tiny mouse. As I stood there I remembered my sword, and pulled it out, thrusting it upwards and into the roof of the serpent's mouth. It opened its jaws in pain, and I flew like a rocket to the door and slammed it closed behind me. Phew!

The Cherubs were close by and they were clapping their hands at my victory. The key was for me to find a part of myself, a soul fragment that was lost. I had a feeling it was to do with the weekend, and my stress.

The little Cherubs scooped me up like a rag doll and carried me deeper into the forest. They lowered me to the ground, and I could see a lion and a lioness patrolling a trap door in the ground.

"It's OK, they won't hurt you" said one of the Cherubs.

The lions were Light Guardians; I wasn't afraid of them. As I moved closer they sat down and I placed my golden key into the lock and entered into the underground world of the Elemental Kingdom. It was fantastic, there were fairies, tiny fairies, shining like 100w light bulbs, I needed sun glasses it was so bright. They were all busy making jewellery and little trinkets in what appeared to be a workshop. There were boxes and boxes of precious gems everywhere you looked; reels of platinum, silver and golden wires. Little Pixies pushing trolleys filled with goodies; I felt like a child in a fairy story.

As I walked along the room, I spotted a woman sitting in the corner facing the wall; she was wearing a brown pointed hat, a bit like a witch's hat. As I got closer, I realised it was me, my soul fragment. I said hello to her, and asked her what she was doing here.

"I made a mistake and I'm sitting in the corner wearing the dunce's hat as punishment" she said.

"It looks like a witch's hat to me" I said. She turned around and the hat had a large letter 'D' on the front of it.

"It doesn't matter that you made a mistake, we all make mistakes, it's important. It helps us to learn. You need to come back"

"I don't want to come back, I can't cope with failure. I'm no good at it". She cried.

"Janine needs you back in order for her to complete her mission, think about her, what do you want to happen?"

"I want her to stop worrying, I feel her worry constantly, and it burdens me."

"She promises to try her best." I said.

At that point, the fragment of me stood up and I held open my arms. She was back in my heart where she belonged, wrapped in a beautiful pink blanket. My journey was over. I closed my eyes, and when I opened them I was with Michael. He carried me up to the white room to see Abba. I had cut negative ties and bonds with Abba before we went into the room. Father asked me to sit on the crystal table.

"Have you decided about your Sainthood?" He asked.

"No Father, I haven't decided. Surely you understand my apprehension after what has taken place over the last few days".

"I do" he said, "I do understand. You will be given another opportunity to win the money."

"What happens if I fail again?"

"Try not to think like that" said Abba

"Okay, thank you for giving me the opportunity"

"You deserve it; you have worked hard my child"

He told me to go home and rest. Michael and I slowly walked down the crystal steps and we said not one word. I knew he was feeling my plight. I knew he was supporting me; he didn't need to tell me. I gave him a hug and I was back.

Before I left for my Tai Chi class, I decided to take some oracle cards out of the pack, asking if there was anything I needed to know. They all directed me towards Source and another initiation. I needed to carry out another clearing when I got home. Tai Chi went really well, we are beginning to flow as a group; it's been six months since I started the classes and I love it. Some weeks I remember the moves and some weeks I'm all over the place, but I still love it either way. This week I asked my higher self to take over, and I only made one or two mistakes in quite a long routine, so it helps. When I got home there was a car near my house with the name 'desire' on the back, and I took it that I should remove negative desires from my system. I was soon lying in a nice hot bath. The first net intent on removing negative desires; it had a large dark box in it. All of my negative desires may have been inside the box or the box was a block around me, I wasn't too sure; I had a tendency not to over analyse stuff, just to remove it. It was taken away by my Angelic helpers and my calibration was up to 3086.

I decided to have a quick chat with Willow before going to see Abba. Willow told me that he was behind me 100% and that he was glad the petition had been granted. He said I deserved another chance, not to worry, and that everything would be all right. I thanked him, and Archangel Michael appeared. He carried me up to the white room, I knocked on the door and entered, Lord Thoth and Sananda were inside deep in conversation with Abba, they stopped talking when I appeared, it kind of makes you feel a bit paranoid when people do that.

"Is everything all right Father?" I asked.

"Yes, but your initiation is overdue and Thoth and Sananda would like to be there". I told Abba that I had a pain in my right ear; he said it was a block caused by me not liking what I was hearing at the weekend. It was an implant created by me that was causing the pain.

"Sananda, please help her remove it" said Abba.

Sananda came to my side and removed four small screws from the side of my head and pulled out a small plate that had formed in my right ear. It felt better immediately, but I think there was an infection in there now that would take a few days to clear up. Once this was done, I thanked Abba for giving me another chance regarding the lottery and my dreams of being the founder of a charitable foundation. I also asked him what would happen if I messed up again. He told me that there was a man who calibrated at 1325 and he would be given the opportunity to receive the trust fund instead of me. I can only do my best I thought, that's all I can do.

Lord Thoth said that the man had not worked as hard as me and told me that he would rather I was placed in charge of the trust. He told me to do my best and said I had a lot of support. We all left the white room except for Abba, and made our way along the stone corridors to the main chamber for my initiation. I wasn't sure why they wanted to come along, these things only lasted a couple of minutes usually. As we walked into the room, the Divine Director called me over to the throne in the centre of the circle. I sat down and immediately something resembling a light bulb was placed in the sole of my right foot. This felt wrong to me, all of my other crystals had been placed in my left side first, not my right.

In my mind, I formed a small grid about the size of a large dinner plate and placed it just below my right knee horizontally. I moved the grid slowly down my leg towards my ankle and foot. It forced the impure light bulb out of my foot. At that moment what appeared to be the Divine Director morphed back into his own form; it was Satan, up to his old tricks. I just laughed and told him that I loved him, and he ran off with a large orb of pink energy following closely behind him. His worst nightmare: my greatest weapon; Love. It weakens the power of darkness. The real Divine Director made his way over to me, my left slipper was removed and a large diamond crystal was placed in the chakra in the sole of my foot. It illuminated the whole of my leg as it settled in.

"Thank You" I said. "What is it for?"

"It is to anchor in your full Goddess energy and ground it; you will receive another one in your right foot tomorrow."

Before I left I asked the Councillors to help me clear the planet of some rather dubious ET's that were causing problems. Of course, they agreed and instantly Mother Earth appeared in the centre of the circle. The first net was full of aliens running wild and shouting.

"Peace be with you", I said to the little creatures and they looked shocked as they were taken away. I thanked the Councillors for helping me and I left. Once outside, I asked Michael if we needed to go and see the Pharaoh; I had heard Egypt mentioned earlier and the Sphinx was in my oracle cards. Lord Thoth also mentioned me being reprogrammed, in order to receive my Saint essence. I looked at him and said. "Saint Essence, I haven't exactly agreed to that as yet"

"Oh" said Thoth, looking rather surprised. Michael looked at Thoth as if to say, she's not to be pushed.

"I'm not going to Egypt tonight. I still need time to think it over, maybe tomorrow. I want to go see the mountain, I'm sure he has a message for me. I said goodbye to Thoth and Sananda and turned around to find White Bear waiting for me on his beautiful flying carpet. I hopped on board and we went to the Mountain. White Bear set me down and left me alone on a crystal balcony made of ice, on the highest point of the mountain. I felt like I was gazing down on the world and I asked the Mountain for a message.

"You are the one they have been waiting for. You hold the key to creation. The creation of the new world; you will teach seven Crystal Ki masters. They too will be given keys. When the time comes, the eight keys will join as one and form the new planets. You are the Saviour; Christ Michael will talk through you. He speaks the word of God. You are that voice" said the wise Mountain.

"How can I do this if I fail, and do not get the trust money I need?" I asked.

"You will not fail".

"Thank you, Mountain". I asked God to bless the Mountain and it was dusted with bliss that looked like fairy dust. I was about to hop back onto the white carpet when I heard an alarm go off outside my bathroom window. I placed a net around the carpet and White Bear, they were taken away. Satan is on my case constantly at the moment, I looked forward to some peace. The real White Bear appeared and he took me home. I gave him a diamond and he was gone. As I lay in my bath pondering what the Mountain had said to me, I noticed Michael was still with me.

"Michael what if I fail?" I asked.

"You will not fail Janine, you have too much support and you need this money to fulfil your destiny. Abba knows that the man who calibrates at 1325 has not worked as hard as you, he does not deserve this trust fund, you do, know it and believe it. That money is yours in trust. You will do the right thing Abba knows that. Now rest!"

53. 5th Nov 2008 – Becoming a Saint

When the electrician arrived this morning, he told me he had to come into Warwick by a different route because the road was blocked. This was a message that there was something in my path. When I went into the bathroom first thing, I noticed that the chain holding the sink plug to the basin had broken, that told me that I had to cut ties with someone. It turned out to be a chain connected to my ex. Once the lights in the kitchen were fixed, the electrician left and I settled down into my morning clearing, in a hot bath with sea salt. I had a feeling that I needed to remove some old ego traits, negative desires, etc. When I set my intentions and pulled a grid down through my body, it was as if I was being peeled like a banana. Layers of negative behavioural patterns and the like were pulled out of my energetic body. I carried on and cleaned my usual toxins and general pollutants created by normal living. The nets were heavy, I was so sensitive to air pollution and the rubbish hanging around in the environment, that I would need to do this clearing nearly every day now unless I stayed at home in my pure space, my bubble; but I had to go outside. I had to work and shop. I went up to 3096 after the clearing but it was not quite enough for my next initiation. Michael pointed towards Willow and said that my trusty friend wanted to talk to me. I walked out of my body and across the bridge to the bottom of my garden. Willow told me that he was glad that I had finally accepted my fate; he referred to me becoming a Saint.

"How did you know I had accepted it?" I asked.

"I can feel your vibration, you have calmed, you have made the right decision, you know that".

I asked him if I was to be allowed one more human relationship and he told me I would, but there would be a lot of work involved to stop them from bringing my vibration down. He told me not to worry about things. I thanked Willow for his support and advice and made my way over to Michael, who placed his arm around my waist and carried me up to the white room.

I knocked on the door and the two of us made our way inside to be greeted by Thoth and Sananda, as well as Abba. Thoth began to clap.

118

"You have accepted your destiny, well done," he said.

I just smiled and walked over to Abba.

"Father, my calibration is not as high as it should be and I have a pain in my upper back".

"Lie down on the table, on your side" he said and instantly he pulled a large chip out of my back and a rod which was the length of my spine. The pain stopped as soon as it was removed; 3102. I was ready. The four of us left and made our way to the chamber at the retreat. I walked over to the throne in the centre of the room and greeted everybody. The Divine Director came over with a crystal on a cushion, and placed it into the base of my right foot but something didn't feel right. As I looked at the crystal, it had a dark metal section in it, similar to a light bulb. I pulled it out of my foot and said, "Nice try Satan" and he was off. The real Divine Director made his way over to me and a large diamond was placed into the sole of my right foot, which illuminated the whole of my right leg. The Goddess energy was grounded through my feet. The initiation was complete, short and sweet and I left the chamber with my comrades. It was time to go to the Pharaoh. We said goodbye to Sananda and Thoth and Michael carried me as we flew along a worm hole to Egypt.

We made our way around to the Sphinx. Just before we entered via the secret passage, I could see the entrance to the temple of the Crystal Skulls flashing through my mind.

"The Skulls are calling me," I said to Michael.

"The Pharaoh first" said Michael.

Once inside, Michael gave Abba's precise instructions to the Pharaoh, which was to remove my negative ego traits and replace them with Saint Essence. I couldn't believe what I was hearing, it sounded so mad, but it was true. I walked to the other side of the room and sat in the chair as usual. The light came in through the roof and entered the crystal egg on the table. Four rays of light emitted from the egg, one above me, one below and one to the right, then left, forming a pyramid. The pyramid then mirrored itself behind me; I was in the centre of a six pointed, back to back, pyramid. This was different to my previous encounters. Above my head a flat disc of light about 1 metre in diameter, began to move down through my body, and it forced out my old ego self, which fell like dust into a tray, on the floor below me. The next thing I could see was the shape of a Saint with a halo at four points around me. They made their way from the points into the centre, into me, my new essence. I remember thinking it would make a good name for aftershave: Essence of Saint. It was done. I gave the Pharaoh a small diamond from my heart to say thank you, but he placed it in his mouth. Weird! I looked at Michael and pulled a net through the Pharaoh to expose a large ET, a soldier, who was removed from the premises. I handed the Pharaoh a replacement diamond which he placed in his third eye, I was satisfied with that, we said thank you and left.

When we got outside, I could feel a sense of urgency regarding the Skulls, and we were immediately on route to Peru, and the temple, via an underground stairwell. These secret passageways were great, they fascinated me. I was like a child when we used them, full of awe and adventure. We made our way down the steps, deep inside the temple, to the circular chamber. As we opened the doors and walked in, we were stopped in our tracks by the vision of some sort of being in the centre of the room. It was a bit like a penguin shape, without the back and feet. Its body shell looked like fibre glass or a silk cocoon. I had never seen anything like it, not even in the movies. There were rays of light, one from each of the skulls; all of them shone like a million candle torches, at the being. They seemed to be holding it prisoner.

Ohman told me it was dangerous, it was trying to steal the Crystal Skull I had rescued. He asked us to remove it. I looked at Michael and he nodded, so a net was placed around the creature and it was removed. An alarm was going off outside, they were still in danger. I placed a larger net around the room which had an egg shape layer of energy around it; this force field had stopped us from entering the room, so we removed that too.

I could still hear an alarm. I panned out my vision using my minds eye; and in the screen, I could see a huge flying saucer surrounding the temple. It too, was netted and taken to Abba. More enlightened souls.

"Thank you Serena", said Ohman "They were trying to steal the Skull, they wanted the power."

"You're welcome", Michael and I said in unison. I asked if there was anything else we could do, and Ohman said, "No, but please take this". A small instrument that looked like a pen with a diamond on top, floated from Ohman across the room to me. He told me to place it in my left wrist. It was a transmitter; we could be in contact no matter where we were, using this device.

"Thank you", I said as I placed it in my wrist and we left.

Later on for some reason I decided to do myself another reading with my oracle cards. The cards told me I was to receive another initiation. I decided to meditate. There was a large black hole in front of me, the void. I'd seen the void many times but they were coming thick and fast this month. I jumped into the blackness head first, as I always did. As I fell into the warmth of the darkness, the Cherubs appeared and carried me towards a large strand of DNA, the double helix, and dropped me into it. As I fell down into the DNA and passed through it, I felt myself being encoded. The world was a distant memory at this point. Ultra speed came into my head. I was being turbo charged, I could feel it, a new ability, warp speed, fantastic. As I tumbled out of the double helix, the Cherubs caught me and took me to the white room, and gently placed me on the floor outside the door at the top of the crystal stairwell. I thanked them, and they flew off, all light and giggles.

Abba told me I needed to go and have my next initiation; I'd hit 3156. He asked me how I was, and I told him I was fine except for my ear ache which was more annoying than painful. I knew it was because I was not listening to my guidance, which was telling me to write more. I have a very short attention span if I'm not on a task I adore, and this was my 3rd book this year. I was looking forward to finishing it, to be honest. Michael and I made our way to the chamber and I sat down on the throne, as directed. Before I could catch my breath, the Divine Director was standing in front of me handing me two large sceptres, one gold, one silver. They were really heavy and something didn't feel right. I turned around and asked Michael to place a net below them. I let go of them and they landed in the net, and were taken away.

"Come on Satan, nice try", I said to the Divine Director. His disguise fell to the ground and he ran like a spring hare out of the room. The real Divine

Director made his way over to me and handed me a beautiful silver cup, a goblet really.

"What's this?" I enquired

"Nectar of the Gods", he replied.

The nectar illuminated my whole body, like a bottle that had captured the sun. It felt heavenly - no, divine; words didn't exist to describe it. I was a lucky so and so, I knew that, the luckiest woman alive.

54. 6th Nov 2008 - The Secret Angel Service

Last night I lay down to sleep, my head started humming like the fan in an old central heating boiler. It was the same most of yesterday afternoon, while I was reading my book, the Time Traveller's Wife. For some reason, my friend, (who had helped me self-publish my book on the internet) said my emails were bouncing straight back to her. Something was wrong. I took my son to college, and when I was driving home I noticed a lady all in black, with long black hair. She was walking on the pavement near to me, she reminded me of a witch. Then, I noticed a couple of buses which said 'not in service', on the front of them.

There was only one or two people I had met over the last few years who I would consider witches, because they actually practised witchcraft. I didn't like it at all, I found it very uncomfortable. I took my oracle cards out when I got home, and asked for some guidance. I must have done something wrong, if I was being sabotaged by a witch; what could I have done? Then, it dawned on me; I had a bar of chocolate on Friday. I was allowed one bar of organic chocolate per month, as a treat. But this one had mint cream inside, which was not allowed.

Eating the wrong food at my level is considered self sabotage, and the universe was reflecting the sabotage back to me. My cards showed a card with a witch on, and the other point that jumped out was, fear of loss. I ran myself a bath, and quickly checked my emails as Abba quite often sent me subtle messages, usually into my junk folder on MSN. I opened the junk folder to two messages which resonated with me. The first said "You got it" which meant I had got the messages earlier, and the second one said "Be ready at the right time". I wasn't quite sure what that meant, but it felt important. I hopped into my warm salty bath and settled in. I cleared the usual pollutants, and then focused on clearing out the fears. The net was full of black rubbish and there were black eggs in there, like frog spawn, only the size of grapes. I felt a lot lighter straight away. I remembered that one of my cards said that I was carrying a large burden, which was weighing me down; and when I checked my back and shoulders, I could see a rusty kind of spiky mattress, stuck to my back. The Angels peeled it off and took it away. It looked like something straight out of a horror movie, a torture chamber even.

The pain in the top of my shoulder eased, it was an instant relief. I had felt burdened lately, but couldn't put my finger on one particular thing, just life really. I asked God and the Angels to fill up all of the gaps with exactly what I needed, and I could see a grid of honeycomb crystals, moving down through my aura. As it moved down, it left tiny crystal deposits in all of the gaps and voids. 3202 popped into my head. Michael carried me up to the door of the white room, still insisting on preserving my energy, by not allowing me to fly. We entered the room and sat down. Abba sat down beside me and asked me how I was? I told him I was fine. We chatted for a few minutes, and then he asked me to lie down on the crystal table, telling me that he wanted to remove some implants from my feet.

I lay down on the table, and he stood at the bottom, next to my feet. He opened the doors on the soles, and removed two implants, that looked like crosses made of metal. He looked at me and said to me in a father's voice.

"Stop worrying about money" and I replied okay.

Michael and I left via the back door, and made our way to the retreat for my next initiation. We entered the chamber and as soon as we stepped across the threshold, everything skipped into slow motion. It was beyond my control and I was taken aback. I asked Michael what was going on. My voice was working at the right speed, as were my thoughts.

"You must sit on the throne at exactly the right time; it is okay, the Time Lords are in control, just relax."

The email flashed into my mind. "Be ready at the right time". That was why Michael was guided to call me, to stop me getting into the bath too early, it made sense now. I slowly made my way towards the throne in the centre of the room; I felt like a puppet, completely in the hands of my puppeteer. I surrendered all control of my body, it was a peaceful feeling. I felt safe, but strange. Once I reached the throne, I sat down and I was cloaked in a tube of light. What looked like a human shape appeared above me. It was a grid of light, a new genetic blue print. It had a halo. It slowly descended and merged with my body. I was a saint or the very beginning of one at least. The tube ascended as soon as it was complete, and I stood up. My strength was gone. I felt like a rag doll, all floppy and weak. Michael caught me, and sat me back on the throne, he told me I needed to go home and rest. My physical body was exhausted with the changes that had been happening over the last few days. He told me that my saint essence had just entered my genetic blue print, and it was essential that I had plenty of rest. I drifted for a moment, and I was home. I lay on the couch and slept soundly for two hours.

Later I flicked over another couple of oracle cards and I got the message that I needed to go and see Abba. I had eaten, so I decided to clear my body of any preservatives or additives that I may have consumed. I lay down on my bed and focused on my breathing; the next thing I knew, I was with Archangel Michael at the top of the crystal stairwell. We knocked on the door and entered the room. My calibration was now up to 3220, I could hardly believe it, really. Abba told me that the Crystal Skulls wanted to see me, and Michael and I made our way to Peru. We entered the temple and wandered along the many stone steps, to the central chamber. Michael stayed just inside the door, as I made my way to the centre of the room.

Ohman greeted me on behalf of the group. He told me that they were grateful for my help, and that they had a gift for me. What looked like a crystal inside two circular rings, floated across to me and rested in my left palm. It reminded me of the marble in the movie 'Men in Black' - the small galaxy (Orion's belt) attached to the cat's collar. When I inspected it further, I could see that it was a galaxy, just like the one in the movie. I said thank you, but I wasn't really sure what to do with such a gift.

Once outside, I handed it to Michael and asked him to take care of it for me. He placed it with the other valuables I had been given, inside his breast plate along with the chip that had been given to me earlier on in the year, (the one that if necessary could destroy the planet, if God willed it); it was still there where Michael had placed it for safe keeping. We decided to go back to the white room to talk to Abba.

"You made a wise choice, giving the galaxy to Michael" said Abba "It will be the home for the new Earth"

"Wow, I'm glad I handed it over in that case." I didn't ask any questions; sometimes, not knowing is for the best. I didn't want to know too much about the future of Earth, my future, or my son's future. It was better left to unfold and be a surprise.

When I was cooking dinner, my friend called me and said that we needed to have a secret meeting. Something was wrong. He didn't say much in case we were being spied on, so I asked Abba to place a sound proof bubble around us, so that we could talk freely. We arranged to meet in a couple of days time, and I texted Tess to see if she could help. She said yes, of course; like me, she always answered a calling. The Secret Angel Service (SAS) were on the case.

55. 7th Nov 2008 – The Milky Bar Cupboard

Michael carried me up to see Abba in the white room; Abba was given a gold key on a ribbon by Sananda, and he leant over and placed it around my neck.

"What's this for?" I enquired, somewhat confused.

"The milky bar cupboard", said Abba. He went on to explain that he was watching me with my son earlier, in the kitchen. My son was eating chocolate and he was teasing me because he knows I can't eat it, because it's toxic to me now. He felt sorry for me, so he invented the milky bar cupboard. Michael pointed to the corner of the room, and I could see a white box with a door and a key hole. At first, I thought they were having a joke with me, but when I turned the key in the lock, lots of little Cherubs the size of my finger, flew out, each one carrying a chocolate, multicoloured chocolates. They were all sorts of geometric shapes.

"They are spiritual chocolates", said Abba "Go on, and try one", he smiled. I held my hand up and a little Cherub popped a pink pyramid into my hand. I put it into my mouth and it was amazing, divine and silky; to be honest. It was the most euphoric taste, not taste feeling, I've ever experienced. Words can't describe it.

"Happy?" said Abba.

"Happy!" I said; I held out my hand and the next one was orange, the last was violet. I stopped at three, anymore than three would spoil the treat.

"Thank you so much Father, they were beautiful, that was so thoughtful of you, thank you." The three of them looked at one another, and smiled. Milky bar cupboards and spiritual chocolates - whatever next?

56. 8th Nov 2008 - You are the new Saviour

Michael said I needed to go and speak to Willow and he told me that a man would be coming into my life soon. My last earthly relationship, but he stated that it was important that the physical side of the relationship was to be kept to an absolute minimum, because it would use up approx 27% of my energy; and because my calibration now affected the local universe as well as Earth, it was important it remained as stable and high as possible. Michael said I needed to go for my next initiation; I was over 3250. We made our way to chambers, and I sat on the throne, as before. The Divine Director came over to me and gave me a cup of nectar. This time it was in a crystal goblet. It looked pure, so I drank it down; it was divine, lighting up my whole body as I drank it. We gave thanks, and left. I wanted to go to see the Mountain, he was calling me. Michael took me, and lowered me down onto the balcony area, at the peak.

"You are the new Saviour" said the Mountain, unprompted. Before my eyes, a beautiful solitaire diamond ring appeared the size of a truck. I was told by Michael then, when the new man arrived, I was to meditate and put the ring on my finger, my wedding finger. "This relationship must be recognised as a spiritual union, because of your status. The ring symbolises this union as blessed, and not just a human coming together of bodies. This man will follow your lead and love you with all of his heart," continued the Mountain. At that moment, a picture of my ex, my sons' father flashed through my mind. I wondered if it was him. I never really loved anyone else, as I did him. I would have to wait and see.

57. 10th Nov 2008 – Remembrance Day

This morning I had a treatment from a friend of mine. When I arrived I warned her that I would cry. I could feel my heart aching with grief. It had been over seven years since my father had died, and yesterday I was reading about the strong spiritual bond between fathers and children. The father is the provider, the protector, the giver of wisdom. The mother is the giver of life, and therefore has a stronger emotional bond. We cut cords with our mothers 4 times throughout our lives 1. Physically - when we are born 2. Mentally - when we go to school 3. Emotionally, when we have our own children 4. Spiritually, when the mother or child dies.

I was thinking about my father a lot, and I realised that I needed to cut the spiritual bond with him, as I lay on the couch having my treatment. I could see his face smiling at me and a silver cord connecting us. I asked Archangel Michael to cut it and said goodbye. I cried like a baby and he was gone. I know he lives on but it is still painful. I miss him so much. I didn't realise how spiritually we were connected, until he died.

When I got home, I pulled out three oracle cards. They informed me that I was being assessed by spirit. I had been through some tests to see if I was to receive the trust fund; it wasn't looking good. I keep making stupid mistakes and I was feeling tired and stressed because of it. I asked Lady Nada if it was going well and she smiled, as if to say, it's going well - so fingers crossed.

We were having our secret meeting tonight. Jon arrived and briefed me on the information he had been given over the weekend, and we discussed it; but I wanted Tess to give us her opinion before we got to work. I had asked Abba to place sound proof shields around us and temporarily, invisibility bubbles, to make sure the dark side could not track us.

Jon drew a picture; it had a large circle in the middle, representing a central courtyard room, which had a portal to the right side of it. There was a wide corridor leading from the main entrance into the central area; then on the other side, another large corridor. The drawing looked like a wrist watch at a glance, with the portal next to the 3 o'clock. The far corridor had doors to the left. Behind these doors were lost souls, captured souls, who needed rescuing. There was a pink door on the far wall; the light warriors would come through, when the time was right.

To the left of the central room, between 7 and 11 o'clock, were dark beings, the leader sat at 9 o' clock. There were two guards at the entrance to the first

130

corridor, with another look out above them. It was a meeting place, and there were others all over the planet, at certain points. The beings were fuelled by the fire energy; it was dangerous and powerful. They had a demonic look about them with curled goat horns. They were planning something big, and it was due to take place tomorrow at 8am - Remembrance Day 11/11/08.

Eight was also significant of infinity. The three of us realised that this was serious stuff, and asked our higher selves to shape shift us to keep us safe. Jon had been holding this information for a few days, and it weighed heavily on his mind. We had been dealing with this type of mission for nearly 3 years, so we were calm about it, but we still treated it with respect, not taking anything for granted. We needed to be safe, we had both been attacked before while we were learning, and the lesson had hit home. This was not a game; we were saving the planet from invasion. Two single mums from Warwick, with hearts of lions. We both loved it though; it defined us, spiritually, anyway. So what if no one knows what we were doing. We knew and God knew, that was good enough for us.

These beings were using the fear of their captives as an energy source. The low frequency vibration, created by Remembrance Day, could also feed them the supply they required. It looked like they were trying to open the portal and bring in demons, but we were only guessing. The portal was heavy duty; it had symbols engraved around the perimeter, similar to the one I had closed down with the Galactic Masters a few months ago, in Dubai. Some portals can be closed with a door and a padlock, but this was seriously dark.

Once we had an idea what we were up against, we sat down, forming a triangle in my lounge. I had placed candles around the room, and we began. The first thing I could see in my mind's eye was stone floors and wall. I was viewing the main entrance corridor; then it just went completely black, all of us were silent, no one could see a thing. I was beginning to get uncomfortable, when Tess and Jon told me they could see the head man looking nervous, as if he could sense something was wrong. We needed to go for it. I had already asked Abba to place a huge cage around the area to catch the ones that might escape. Our code to net them was firefly and Tess had the large nets thrown over them. I could see a four headed dragon as I captured the leader and bound him in a net. He struggled, but he was trapped. The dragon and the others were surrounded in a large net, and removed from the scene. Jon had been given a new tool, it was a water gun; like a fireman's hose, it sprayed salt water. These creatures thrived on fire energy, so water was our best weapon. We decided to ask God to bless it to make it even more powerful.

While I worked with the Galactic Masters to seal up the portal, Jon sprayed the whole area, and Tess opened the doors and released the trapped souls. I could see them running in every direction; they were blind from being locked in the dark for so long. I was close to tears for them, they had suffered so much. Once the portal was closed and sealed, Tess could open the pink door at the far end of the corridor. The light warriors flooded into the area.

Jon spotted a pair of eyes in the 9 o' clock position; it was a large beetle, possibly linked to Master Zed, if not him. We did not have time to check. I threw a net around him, and he was gone. There was a large long haired devilish creature 20ft high, making his way towards Jon, it just walked out of the wall; there must have been a secret passage way. I heard Tess say that I should open up two clearing vortexes like tornados; one to help the lost souls go into the light, and one to suck up the dark. I invoked the wind and they were formed. The large creature retreated back into the wall. Tess could see it escaping along the passageways with lots of the other beings. I grabbed the end of the tunnel as if it were a hose pipe, and began to squeeze it closed, forcing them back towards the circle; it had formed a black hole in the wall by this stage and the entrance was covered in black tar. As soon as they came through it, they were sucked into the vortex, which had a large cage on the top where they were trapped, until it was time for them to be taken into the light.

At the far end, the clearing vortex was much softer and full of warm gold white light. The angels were taking some of the souls through the opening and others left via the pink door. It was a mass panic, with people running and screaming. We had to keep our wits about us - we were not finished yet. Jon said that this forum or meeting place was somewhere up north. Immediately Edinburgh Cathedral came to my mind, and I could see it. This was a small part of a much more major network; they were using the ley lines as connections between different churches and cathedrals. They were fuelled by fire energy. I've doubted the purity of fire energy for years; I never used it because of that doubt. I asked Jon to spray the cathedrals and churches; he had one eye on them, and the other on the initial forum; a true top gun tactic - split screen.

He told me he could see a group of the beings clambering up a stairwell, not far below the portal area. I had them netted. More and more souls poured out into the corridors, bewildered and terrified. It was sad to see them, but we had no time to comfort. I told

133

them we were light workers sent by God to help, and to try and calm them, but they could not hear me.

As I looked at the Cathedral again, I could see two gold cogs and rings in the sky, immediately above the building. It was a time space portal of some sort; it was an entry/exit point for the invaders. I told Jon and Tess, and we decided to close them all. They were everywhere; above the Vatican, the White House, schools, hospitals; it was shocking - a major invasion. We grouped them into priority order, and squashed the portal flat, folded it in half, then quarters, and then removed, in nets. The black dust residue was washed with huge waves of salt water; this exercise was in the hands of God and the Angels.

Jon spotted a large bolt through Mother Earth with a nut at the bottom.

"That has to go" he said. I undid the nut and the globe collapsed, then the whole thing was taken away; it was a layer of deceit; a false planet, red herrings created by the armed forces and the government, to distract people from the truth. We decided to pray; we asked God to bless, heal and purify Africa, the President and all of the powerful leaders. Bless, heal and purify, over and over, seven times. We could see white energy, like snowflakes, covering all of them, it was fantastic.

Just as we thought we had finished. I spotted a space ship; the bottom opened. I knew it was light when I saw the chain lowered down, and a tiny silver ant climbed out. I had seen these light workers before. They were shiny like chrome and had large light blue eyes. They made their way down to the surface of the planet, and placed another figure of eight tube of God consciousness around Mother Earth. They had placed the first one in there, when they worked with me in

134

Dubai. I explained this to Tess and Jon while they were working. These guys took me onto their ship one afternoon while I was resting on my hotel bed. Everything on board hovered; it was amazing. I felt really honoured. Once they were done, they climbed back up the chain and into their ship, and were gone.

"And they said it could not be done" said Archangel Michael. We didn't know who he was talking about, and none of us asked. The whole exercise had taken us nearly 2 hours and we were all shattered. Tess went home and I put the kettle on. Back to reality.

58. 11th Nov 2008 - The Second Coming

I went to bed crying and I woke up crying. I can't believe I've blown my second chance at receiving that trust fund. When I was driving my son to college I passed four vans with St Nicholas written on the side and then a large truck with its hazards flashing and the words 'security' along the side of it. It looked like a message saying I would feel more financially secure by Christmas, I hoped it was anyway. A lot of publicity via the media was about to come my way and hopefully my book would be out there where it needed to be. I was still really low and I cried all the way to college and back. When I got home, I ran a hot bath. I needed to speak to Abba. I asked my angels to help me remove fear in the first net and then anxiety. It looked like a black box in the net as it was taken away. My third eye had a sword sticking out of it, my crown had daggers stabbed into it; all attracted by my negative state of mind. I had to clear myself before I got any lower.

Once cleared, I went to speak to Willow. He told me I looked terrible, really low, and advised me that all was not lost. I should go and speak to Father and tell him how I felt and ask for mercy; maybe even another chance. He was a merciful God after all. Michael arrived, placed his arm around my waist and carried me up to the white room. As we got to the door I shape shifted into the beautiful white Fairy I had transformed into yesterday; I was glowing a brilliant white energy.

Inside the room were Lord Thoth and Sananda in their usual seats. I went to sit next to them but Abba called me over to him and asked me to sit on the table.

"Your depression is being felt throughout the whole galaxy, my child. You do not realise your power. Let it go, let the pain and worry go now" said Abba softly.

"Father, I have messed up less than 24 hours after my second chance, by a stupid remark to a woman who already knows I am an Enlightened Master, why am I treated so severely?"

"It is not what she knows; it is who is around when you talk. You put yourself at risk. Only the other day you received a message saying that there are spies everywhere and they want to stop you. Do you understand?"

"I do now, I'm so sorry Father, please show mercy on me and give me another chance"

He held up a piece of paper and said, "Look, a second petition in your defence, why should I grant this petition?" I looked down towards the floor like a scorned child then glanced over to Thoth and Sananda, hoping they would answer on my behalf. They both looked at me with so much love in their eyes; I began to cry.

"Father, you should grant the petition because you know I deserve it", I mumbled my voice shaky and weak. He looked towards Sananda and Thoth; they both nodded. He looked at me and agreed to their wishes. I was to get another chance.

"Now, let this go," said Abba "Go and receive your initiation with Michael". I hugged him tightly and thanked him, then left with Michael. As I walked past Sananda and Lord Thoth, I winked at them and they both smiled back at me.

Once we were at the retreat, as we walked along the stone corridors, I asked Michael if I was the right person for this job. He told me I was the only person and that we needed to visit the Mountain. We went into the chamber and I sat on the throne in the centre of the room; Lady Nada walked over to me and placed her hand on mine.

"We are all supporting you" she said.

"Thank you, I need it" I replied. The Divine Director came over to me with a crystal chalice and he gave it to me, I pulled a small net through the cup of nectar and there was a layer removed, it was not pure. Lady Nada walked away and quickly returned with a new chalice.

"This one is pure", she said and handed me the nectar. I drank it down and as before the light filled my whole body, like a beacon, it was stunning. I said thank you and we were on our way to the Mountain. I stood on the crystal balcony gazing down into the dark valley below, so deep you could not see the bottom. I asked the wise Mountain for some words of wisdom.

"You are the one, you are the saviour, you must not worry", said the Mountain. I turned to Michael and asked him what this meant. I was under the impression that all of the people with their higher hearts functioning were the second coming. Yet here, the Mountain keeps telling me that I am the one, the Saviour; I didn't understand.

"Sananda and Abba chose one to be their voice, that one is you. You are the channel for Sananda to come again, Abba will speak through him via your body. You will speak the word of God." I turned away from Michael and looked out towards the vastness of the universe.

"No pressure then?" I said and turned back to look at him.

"No pressure" he said and we both laughed "You will be fine, do not worry". And I was home.

59. 12th Nov 2008 - White fibre optics

About 8pm I decided to have a bath and clear more fear from my system. I could see a black hook in my right shoulder blade; a chain lead down to a concrete block. I could do without that weight to drag along. Michael pulled out the hook and the block was removed. Once I had cleaned that, Michael took me to see Abba; he wanted to reprogram my DNA.

I lay down on the crystal table and Sananda walked over to my feet. He opened the door to my sole chakras and white fibre optics grew out and down to my earth star, wrapping themselves tightly around it. My new essence was being grounded in; the glass looking tube of light formed around me, and before Abba began I asked him to remove all memories of the lottery scenario, to help me get over the stress it has caused. He just looked at me and carried on with the treatment. My calibration was up again, this time to 3402.

60. 13th Nov 2008 - ET's, goblins and spirits

I had a really uncomfortable feeling in my chest, like heartburn, but more spread out. When I got around to my clearing I could see a large wire with lots of broken smaller wires sticking out, like electrical wire. My main meridian was severed again. I could see a large gold yellow anchor half in half out of my solar plexus, it looked nice, but it felt heavy. It was attached to someone I had spoken to on the telephone earlier today. I pulled it out, and I could see that it was black inside; this person's shadow self was trying to drain my energy. They looked pretty miffed when I spotted them. I seem to have the ability to see both people's light and dark self when I'm in meditation. We all have a shadow, thankfully mine is the size of a finger these days, but it still exists. I asked my angels to help reconnect the wires and replace the plastic sheath over them. The heartburn was gone instantly. 3408.

I had a 666 message earlier, so I called on Lady Nada and the Karmic Board, and we pulled three nets through Mother Earth. The first one had over 20,000 ET's, goblins and spirits in it; they were really hyper, so I sent a bubble of peace into the net to calm them down. The second net had a large black box which represented fear. The third was negative sexual energy and full of red worms, Yuk! I asked Abba to fill all of the gaps with exactly what was needed and could see a wave of crystals stars and geometric shapes falling like snow onto the planet. It was so beautiful.

A large black hole formed before me and I dived in head first. I fell into the black creamy void, deeper and deeper into infinite darkness, in order to reach the light. A large hand caught me as I was transforming into a flower, then an angel. It was the hand of God, my saviour. He placed me on his shoulder and showed me lots of images of my future. It looked fantastic, large audiences listening to my talks, me playing in the sand, my son smiling. My book a huge success, I was a respected author and spiritual teacher.

"You are nearly there; the worst is behind you now. You have achieved more than any human before you" said Abba as we watched my future unfold.

"I want to serve you and make you happy Father."

"You have excelled all expectations. I am very happy. In a few days, you will be a Saint. Relax, your future is written, your dreams will come true."

"Thank you Father" I replied.

61. 14th Nov 2008 –
10,000 diseases and 500,000 drugs

Last night I dreamt I could see a man standing on the top of a scaffolding tower carrying a large box on his shoulders. As I watched him, the weight toppled him backwards and he fell to the ground. Not dead, but injured. I ran to a telephone and three times I tried to call for an ambulance, but I was getting a wrong number. Then I used my mobile and got through. I don't remember anything after that. This dream could mean two things 1. I had fallen, meaning I had made a mistake by talking to Jon on the telephone about our meeting on Monday, or 2. I had been hurt and my communication channel was damaged.

When I woke up the first seemed to be the one I was leaning towards. I just thought "Oh well"; I was relieved to let it go, but something told me to pick some oracle cards out, and they seemed to imply that

I still had a chance regarding the trust fund; and the second meaning was the correct one. We would have to wait and see, I guess. Later, I was reading on the internet that before we had pharmaceutical medicines, there were only 7 main diseases and 10 plants that could treat them. Since the invention of chemical medicine, we now have approximately 10,000 diseases and half a million drugs to treat them. I was thinking; no wonder we have more cancer, diabetes and other horrible illnesses with all of those chemicals floating around inside of us, not to mention food preservatives and additives. Before these were invented, we had natural organic foods carrying their own sugars, fats, proteins etc. I read that metal toxins can cause MS; that dairy products can lead to breast and prostate cancer. It's shocking when you wake up and start to investigate what's really going on.

My clearing was late today, lunch time. All week I had been noticing signs that I couldn't figure out; pictures of trees, the words quantum, ancestor and family. My distant cousin in Australia had written to my mum trying to trace her family tree. I cleared my stomach and heart chakra of a huge anchor, (attached by grief to my father), then a large spinning top type chip just below my heart. I realised I needed to do some work on my family. Also my worry had attracted some daggers that must have been floating around in the atmosphere. I still had a round mass in the lower left side of my stomach. When I asked Michael what it was, he said that it was an apple, a black apple. Apples reminded me of Adam and Eve's temptation.

"It's Sin" he said.

Then it hit me, I need to do some ancestral healing, the sins of my father's type of stuff. That's what the messages were about, the quantum field and my family tree. They wanted to be cleaned as well. They were all around me. The past and the future coexist; we are all here and now. I carried out some clearing on all of them. They were smiling and I asked God to fill the gaps; a huge ball of light passed through me and split into two balls, one behind me and one in front of me, through all of my relatives. The healing was done, I had reached 3466.

"We need to go to the Pharaoh," said Michael "and then to chambers"

The Pharaoh was asked to program me with more Saint Essence, and I sat in the usual place. As did last time, the light formed a double pyramid shape around me. A small circular grid came down through me, cleaning out old ego essence into a small tray below me. It had a bit of dust in it, not much really. Then, from the six points, the blue print of a Saint began to glide towards me, and merged into my essence. It was done.

I gave the Pharaoh a diamond which he put to his mouth and bit, like a back street jeweller. I looked at Michael and we pulled a net through Pharaoh, to reveal a large gremlin type ET. He was taken off, and I replaced the diamond which the real Pharaoh placed in his brow. When we walked to the chamber and opened the doors, I was blinded by a large golden white orb of light, nearly as big as me. As my eyes adjusted I could see that it was a rather impressive Fairy, with what looked like a tape measure in her hands. As I sat on the throne she hovered around me, above me, and below me, measuring me with her tape. She even measured my scalp.

"For the crown" said Michael "She is taking measurements for your new attire." I was less confused now, and she disappeared. Abba walked over to me, he was glowing whiter than white for some reason, maybe he just stood out more in the chamber than he did in the white room, I'm not sure. He handed me a pure clear crystal glass with light in it, and I drank it down; then I began to cry.

"Tomorrow is your big day, you will be crowned a Saint" he said to me, as he handed me a handkerchief. "Now go home and relax"

62. 15th Nov 2008 – Patron Saint of light workers

I had to go and se Abba, I spoke about my ex and because it was considered gossip I had just lost £33 million as a result. I looked at Abba and said,

"Father, are you going to show me that you are the merciful God I believe you to be, and wipe the slate clean of this misdemeanour?" He was fighting giving in to my plea, but he did.

"Thank you, I love you" I said.

At the other end of the room a step ladder appeared. I felt I had to climb it. It led me through a trap door into another completely white space; it was not a room because it did not have walls. It was an infinite white space, that's all I can say about it. I could see Lady Nada and the Karmic Board sitting in a circle. She called me to join them. We needed to do a clearing on the local universe; there were lots of alien life forms causing chaos, not evil, but naughty teenage type of stuff, a problem nevertheless.

The first net had more than 21,000 souls in it, they were taken into the light, Abba's choice, not ours. We also cleaned fear and greed, while we were there.

I made my way back down into the white room, said goodbye to Thoth and Sananda, and left with Michael. When we got outside the room the crystal staircase had turned into an amazing slide and we jumped on board, slipping and sliding like children laughing. I needed to laugh, I really needed to laugh. I felt like I was carrying the world; no, the universe on my shoulders. When we bumped into one another at the bottom, Michael looked at me and said,

"You could charm the birds from the trees" and I grinned triumphantly. Time for tea!

I was in the habit of having two baths a day now, and today was no different. I received a message via my oracle cards to go to Abba; he wanted to work on my DNA. Thoth and Sananda were in the white room again; everyone seemed in good spirits. I lay down on the crystal table and the test tube of light surrounded me, the layers passed through me and it sparkled like a crystal firework.

"Perfect", said Abba, "3504"

My big day, my Saint initiation was about to happen.

"What is your chosen skill?" he asked. I'd almost forgotten about that: I was due a new ability, a superhuman ability.

"Teleportation, please", I replied. He pointed to the back door. I walked over to it, opened it and could see a sheer drop, a black hole. I dived in, falling, flying, floating, all three. As I began to think it would never end, the Cherubs grabbed me, and lead me to the giant strands of DNA. I was dropped in and slid down the tube, and out of the bottom. They looked at me and quick as a flash, I was gone. I landed in the white room, flash, flash; I was teleporting like a mad

144

woman, not great distances but behind Sananda to next to Abba. It was fantastic.

"Slow down child", said Abba "It uses up a lot of energy; energy you need."

I could teleport, what a buzz!

Later I went for a treatment from my friend Tess. She repaired damage to my neck and comforted me in a past life situation. I had been hanged for what, we didn't know. She also found a small girl, lost and in the dark, in my solar plexus; a soul fragment of me. Tess asked the angels to bring in the light, and they guided her back into my heart. Once she had tweaked and poked and prodded, I was balanced. I was still a bit low on energy, but I had asked Abba for a holiday and I just needed to trust it would happen. He was running my life now, not me.

She asked me to stay and work with her on her last client. His energy was high. Just before he arrived the room cooled, a double kind of spirit came before him, and stood waiting, watching our every move. They told me he was a High Priest and he was to be an important spiritual teacher in the future; he calibrated pretty high. He was just a normal guy, open minded but not a spiritual person, not in service anyway. He was full of chips, text book chips. He had rods in his hips and legs, and remnants of ritualistic torture; a rack with spikes in his back, barbed wire around his hips. It took the two of us almost an hour and a half to clear him. I placed a diamond in his brow chakra, God consciousness. He was little shocked by it all, but content in the knowledge that it was for his highest good. I often did a swap treatment with Tess, no money changed hands. I thanked her, and left around 10:20pm. Time for my initiation. I ran myself a bath and settled in. It was about 10:45pm. Archangel

Michael told me I needed to wait unit 11pm, they were expecting me then.

As I lay in the hot water, I could hear shouting outside in the street, a man and woman arguing. I asked God to bless them, but they were hard at it. I checked the area around my house and I could see small ET's all over the place, like teenagers looking for mischief. They were obviously affecting the behaviour of the couple, adding fuel to the fire so to speak, so I netted the whole area, and had them taken away. The noise stopped; it was calm and peaceful, and I settled down again.

Michael took me up to the white room where the glowing creature that had taken my measurements, eagerly awaited me; a long white robe decorated from the waist up in gold thread and diamond gems; a true work of art. Two or three Cherubs helped me don the regal attire, and placed silver slippers on my feet. They brushed my long wavy copper hair, and I was ready.

"You look beautiful", said Michael.

"Beautiful, just beautiful", said the little helpers.

We made our way to the retreat, the doors opened and as we stepped inside, I could see light beings as far as my eyes could see. Just about everyone in who's who had turned up. I felt like royalty. I was asked to sit down on the throne, and immediately a crystal tube of light surrounded me. For a moment I was blank, free, no-mind, ecstatic. Then I could see the image of Saints above, slowly lowering into my being. My head was light; a high pitch humming noise radiated into my crown, and down through my whole being. I was euphoric for a minute or two. This Saint energy felt great, but living in the 3D worlds and

146

holding it, was not going to be easy. I wasn't being naive about it. I had a lot of work ahead of me. Abba walked over to me, a beautiful crown in his hands. At that moment a cage appeared about me and wrapped itself around me. It was Satan; he was trying to cause problems again. Michael stepped in and cut the cage free.

"I give you Saint Serena, Patron Saint of light workers", said Abba as he placed the crown on my head. There was applause and music, trumpets blasting. It was fantastic, I had done it. Little old me. As we made our way into the banquet hall I asked Abba why Satan had been allowed to interrupt the proceedings, and he simply said, "Free Will; he keeps you on your toes" and we both smiled.

The banquet really was fit for a king. I sat at Father's left, Michael and Sananda to his right. We feasted on goodies; pink chocolate for me specially ordered, only three, of course. Goblets of light, Angels played harps. We ate, drank and chatted for a while, and I asked if I could be excused. It was nearly midnight and I was tired. Abba agreed I needed to rest; I was about to try and sneak out quietly when he announced.

"All stand, our honoured guest is about to leave us".

I stood up looked at the wave of light and said, "Thank you, thank you to Michael, Sananda, Lady Nada, Lord Thoth, all of my guides and helpers. Thank you to the animals for their essence, and thank you to the trees, the mountains and everyone who had ever guided me, or protected me. I love you all, may God bless every one of you", I turned to Abba, "Most of all, thank you for giving me life Father, I love you and promise to serve you to my best ability now and always, thank you."

147

63. 16th Nov 2008 - Sirius and the UFO

I recently had been handed books to read by a couple of friends of mine, both fiction. One was about a time traveller (a love story); the other was about a prostitute (also a love story). I don't generally read fiction, but I do make a point of reading books that are placed in my hand, as this is a sign that there is something in them I need to know, or learn from.

I now had a super human ability, the ability to time travel. I took a sneaky preview of my future and I looked happy enough, I didn't want to know too much.

The book about the prostitute was interesting. She fell in love with a man who touched her soul, an artist; she had not even slept with. The other man she was involved with taught her about sadomasochism (S&M). The pain, suffering and pleasure, without fear, took her into the void, the same void I had entered many times through healing and mediation. I had never really understood S&M before, but now I felt I did. It was not for me, but I felt that by reading this I now had a more profound understanding. The void was the doorway to the next level of consciousness; it brought you closer to God, into a state of euphoria.

After my morning clearing I went to speak to Willow; I talked to him about the S&M in the book I had been given. He informed me that I was learning to transcend right and wrong, non judgement. The next thing I could see was a black hole and I jumped in; as I was falling I felt free but then four dark grey gremlin type creatures grabbed me, and started to push me around. I was surprised at first, then a net surrounded me and I heard Michael say "Father does not want you to go there." He lifted me up and placed me on the ground beside him. Another black hole appeared and Michael pointed towards it, I jumped again. I fell into the abyss of tranquillity and the Cherubs caught me this time, and took me to the white garden. White animals surrounded me; they all had pale blue eyes, like pools of unconditional love from a far off galaxy.

Abba was sitting on the marble bench nearby; I made my way over to him, the animals followed. I asked him about the first black hole. He told me I should look before I leap; lesson learned. We discussed the book and I concluded that the soul has a plan that involves many different experiences for many different people. The journey consists of all sorts; people who take the highs and lows to extremes, and those who glide along on the equator of life; there is no right and wrong behaviour, or decisions, only consequential choices.

This filled me with a peace, the knowledge that the mistakes or wrong choices I had made in my life were not wrong at all; they were simply choices, all part of my journey. Some people choose to differ more than others in order to grow. The prostitute did not need to be rescued, it was her choice. She would rescue herself when her time was right. I asked him why I kept seeing the word Luck or Lucky on my computer, or in TV programmes.

"Lady Luck has something for you", he said and a beautiful light being appeared, and placed a large white horseshoe around my neck. I must be lucky now. It became part of my essence. The next thing we knew, Fairy Godmother was there, asking me to make a wish. I wished that all of my books were successful, the more money they made, the more I would have to give away.

I popped out to get some provisions, and on my way to the shops I noticed a man wearing a black coat, over his camouflage jacket. There must be something around my aura. A car drove toward me with no head lights on; it was dark. I spotted 666, a call to service; I wondered what it would be this time. As I paid the cashier, my eyes were guided toward a magazine which had 'fusion' on the front. I would need to fuse with Archangel Michael, whatever it was. When I got home, I quickly checked my aura and sure enough, there was a dark brown egg surrounding me way out in my aura. I removed it. My neck was aching and I spotted the word 'transformer' a couple of times.

I was soon in the bath tub on my way to the white room with Michael. Abba informed us that there was a problem on Sirius, caused by an attempted ET invasion. Michael and I fused our power and we travelled through a portal, to Sirius.

The territory was green and pleasant, but we were standing on top of a huge plug, like a waste plug in a sink; it was 20 metres at least. We made our way to the edge, and cut it free from the ground; it had been sort of welded into position. Michael cut the large chain, which leads from the centre up into the sky, and was connected to a saucer shape UFO. He netted the ship and it was taken to Abba.

64. 18th Nov 2008 – The Goddess of War

I took my son to college, and again this morning I noticed a large white van with the word 'ASD Metal Services' on the sides. ASD stood for autistic spectrum disorder, a category I considered myself and my son to be in. Metal services could have meant metal toxins or some sort of metal contraption that needed removing on an energetic level. I asked what it meant; the next van that jumped out at me had 'dynarod' on the side, so I knew it was referring to metal rods. These things were placed in us before we were born to block certain esoteric knowledge being accessible, until we were ready for it. When I asked Abba whether they were in me or my son, I spotted a coach with the words 'VIP' on. This was just one of the names Abba had for me when sending these 3D signs. Sometimes it was diamond, star, tree, a large white van, and princess, amongst others. I realised that I needed to remove the rods. When I got home, I ran myself a bath and settled in. There was a lump in my throat, and I could see a brown egg around my blue pearl; once it was cleaned, the tension in my throat was gone. I called on my angels to help remove the rods. Two angels, one above the other, pulled them up and out of my spine, at my neck area. There were 36 rods about 1 metre in length. My back felt less tense once they were moved. I also had a large hook into the back of my heart which was connecting my ex partner to me. Michael cut the chain and I said, "I cut and release you, with love and peace, I am totally free", to release the energy.

Michael carried me up to the white room; we knocked on the door and made our way inside. Thoth and Sananda were talking to Abba, they all looked concerned.

"What is wrong Father?" said Michael as we both sat down.

"Sanita, the Goddess of War from sector 14 has declared herself no longer a light worker and informed me that she wishes to join Satan and Callagastia."

We all looked at one another and asked what did this mean for mankind.

"It could cause a lot of damage to the ascension process of the planet, more wars, more destruction, more fear, more hatred, she is powerful." said Abba.

"What can we do?" I asked.

"I want you to speak to her as a group. She will be here shortly". At that moment, I thought, if she is not going to listen to God, she is not going to listen to us. Then I realised; she's a woman, I'm a woman.

"Abba, do you want me to talk to her because I am also a woman?"

"Yes", he said.

There was a knock at the door and this long legged, stunningly beautiful warrior walked into the room. She came over and sat down next to me. Abba introduced me to her; I was the only person she did not know. I could sense a prickly dark egg shaped energy around her body. I held my hand out and she shook it. Immediately, the prickly energy surrounded me and I quickly removed it in a net. It was a spell I could feel it. She looked shocked, stunned even, as if she had just awoken from a deep sleep.

"Are you ok?" I asked.

"What happened?" she asked.

"When you took my hand, the spell that had been placed in your energy field was absorbed by me, and I have removed it."

Abba looked at her and asked her how she felt. She said that she wasn't sure; she said she felt like she had been asleep.

"I take it that you will not be joining Satan and Callagastia?" Abba asked her.

"No, never Father", she replied, still shocked at her loss of control.

"They tried to trick you into joining them, to slow down the ascension process planned for this universe", he told her.

"I am sorry Father", she stood up and walked over to Abba.

"Worry not Sanita, it was no fault of yours, all is well, you need to go and rest."

She shook my hand again and thanked me; said goodbye to Michael, Thoth, and Sananda and left the room.

"All is well, Michael take Serena to the void".

Michael and I made our way out of the room via the back door, and into a lift. Michael said that we needed to visit the Mountain first. When the lift doors opened, there we were at the balcony on the Mountain. I asked the Mountain for some words of wisdom.

"You are the Saviour, your destiny is about to begin and unfold before you. You have a very important job to do. It is necessary that you cleanse yourself daily and keep the people around you at a distance." The wise Mountain informed me.

"Thank you Mountain." I replied.

We stepped back into the lift and the doors opened on the other side; black, black and more black, the void. I jumped into the velvet darkness and felt a sense of freedom, peace, euphoria, falling without control or fear, until I was caught gently by the five Cherubs. They carried me in a white blanket and placed me on the lawn in the heavenly garden. I was naked, born again. As I stood up, a white robe formed around me.

65. 19th Nov 2008 - The Elders from Sirius

I didn't get the chance to do my daily cleaning until half way through the day. It was the usual stuff. Michael said we were needed in the white room and when we entered, there were four small crystals beings seated opposite Abba. They were half of our size, they were not human looking, no facial movement, they looked like they were sculpted from hundreds and hundreds of tiny crystal wands, quartz even. They were clear like ice. Michael stood near the door and I sat down. Abba proceeded to tell me that they were the Elders from the Elemental Kingdom on Sirius. They had come to thank the warriors who saved them from invasion.

Abba gestured toward me, and then translated their gratitude. I in turn gestured to Michael; there were two of us after all. The beautiful little beings then made their way out of the back door and they were gone. I looked at Abba, he was not himself. I could feel his sadness. The invasion of Sirius, the Goddess of War, Satan's constant interference was making him sad; his aura was not as shiny as it should be,

"Lie down Father, let me treat you." I said.

"Thank you, my child", he climbed onto the crystal table and Michael and I pulled a grid down through him to disperse the lower frequency energy, then we collected it in a net and called on all of the angels and Saints asking them to bless Abba. It worked, the blessings came, and the energy was magnificent. His aura was restored and he was smiling as he got to his feet.

"Thank you that feels much better", he said.

"It's the least we can do Father, the least."

66. 20th Nov 2008 - The Clock

Last night I dreamt about a bus with the word "EXIT EARTH" on the front of it. While I was cooking dinner, I turned on the radio and they were talking about time travel. It looked like another calling.

Michael took me to the white room. Abba said he had a mission for us: we were to travel into the future.

"I would like you to go to the museum in the crystal city on Jupiter. There is a clock in a crystal case, in the centre of the main hall. Bring me the clock. Here is the key to the case." He handed me a small gold key.

"Anything else Father?" I asked.

"No, just bring the clock."

We left and flew through a worm hole, out of this universe around the outside wall, and back in; we arrived on Jupiter. The city was a few miles away. Michael opened a trap door in the ground and we were flying along through brightly lit corridors. Another trap door and we were in the main hall of the museum. The clock was exactly where Abba said it would be, in a case in the centre of the room. I went over to it, opened the case and took out the clock, locking the case behind me. The clock was not what I expected at all. It was a crystal ball about 8 inches in diameter with gold cogs, wheels cast inside and a gold rod straight through the main axis. I handed it to Michael, and we were homeward bound. I asked what was so special about this clock, and he said that it

155

altered the Time/Space continuum; what that meant I wasn't sure. Once back at the white room, Michael gave me the clock; we went inside and handed it to Abba. He looked very pleased and placed it into his heart. Our job was done, I made my way home.

67. 22nd Nov 2008 - Source

It took me forever to get to sleep last night. I tossed and turned for hours. This morning I turned on the computer to check the lottery results, and guess what? I hadn't won!

I expected to be distraught, but to be honest I was indifferent. The last couple of months of trying and being tested were wearing me down to the point where I couldn't care less about the lottery. So that was that.

I ran myself a hot bath cleaned my energetic bodies and asked Michael to take me to see Abba. When I asked him why I hadn't won he told me it was because of my attachment to the outcome. I don't know a man or woman alive who if they were told that they were going to win £33 million in the lottery would be able to detach from it. It's ridiculous. I told Abba I was fed up trying, and that he should give it to someone else. I couldn't take anymore let downs. I was exhausted and consumed by it. I began to cry, I had a lump of anger in the back of my heart that was really hurting me. I needed to let it go and crying helped.

I drifted into another place, the rooms where my other personalities resided. I spoke to my physical body that was tired and had back ache: I promised to rest and do some healing on my back. I went to see my emotional self who, as usual, just needed to hug. My mental body looked terrible; she had two huge lumps the size of oranges on the top of her head. Too much stress, it looked explosive. I visualised a white syringe draining the stress out of the lumps and she said she wanted to read a good book, no problem, I can fix that. My spiritual body was cowering in the corner, looking abandoned and frightened. When I asked her what she needed, she said she wanted to listen to beautiful music, and reminded me that I had missed my last two Tai Chi classes; she loved them. I told her I would definitely go this week, and would make a point of listening to some more music. My higher self who looked more like my God self these days, reminded me that I was the Saviour and that my feelings were powerful: my vibration was felt throughout the whole universe; therefore I needed to be calm and peaceful. Stop worrying, everything will be fine.

The next thing I knew, I was back with Abba and Michael. Abba asked Michael to take me to the void. I loved jumping into the void, passage through fear. He showed me out of the back door and into a lift. The doors opened on the far side. It was black, not complete blackness, but a black hole. I looked back at Michael.

"It's safe", he said and I dived into the hole. I glided head first through what seemed like a mile of tubing; then I was headed toward a light, and I was there. Source. I stopped dead in the centre of the brightest golden white light you could imagine. My image, my body became source; I lay still, everything ceased to exist.

I was one with God. I floated in all of its purity, I let it energise and engulf me. I was at peace. There I stayed until the water was cold, and I was back, home, happy, enlightened.

68. 23rd Nov 2008 - Faith

Frog came out in my oracles today; that means cleansing. I ran a bath and settled in. I pulled lots of worms and parasites out in the first net. It was necessary after a visit to the supermarket; energetically, they're filthy places. I also had the initiation card, so a trip to the retreat was imminent. 3598, a few more blessings and I would be over the 3600. I lay there and simply asked Abba to bless, heal and purify me on a cellular level, seven times and voila, I hit 3601 - simple when you know how.

Soon it was time for my next initiation. I asked Abba why I had to raise my vibration yet higher still. I thought I could rest at 3500. He told me that I handled the power well, and the universe needed me as powerful as possible. Fair enough, I thought, but a part of me missed being normal.

When I was having my evening bath, I found hooks and lines from my heart to my sacral chakra, and removed them. 3626. Abba and I went to the white garden. He told me that I had passed my tests and all was well. He showed me a holographic image of myself, looking radiant, I was smiling and happy. The business with the lottery had still damaged my faith though, he knew that. He called Faith, and she wrapped me in a blanket of her energy. I felt a lot better. We sat for a while hand in hand; then I came back. I can understand why Sananda spends so much time in that garden. It really is divine.

69. 24th Nov 2008 – Make a Wish

Tess and I were carrying out a double treatment on a friend of hers. Clare had a chip in her stomach, which was linked to a UFO. They had been using her for some time. She said she felt as though she was reporting back to someone. It turned out that she was; she had a camera type chip in her third eye, which was allowing the aliens to remote view everything, and to keep up to date with the progress of the light workers and the ascension progress. This gave them inside information, and they not only stole her energy but the energy of people connected to her. We had to do a major tie cutting, burn all contracts, bonds, pacts and agreements she may have made with them, not only in this life, but past lives. Tess could feel the anger of the aliens as we cut the negative connections. They were not happy. Tess felt that they were connected to the clearing we had done with Jon, when we closed portals all over the planet and captured what I now believe to be, a group of low frequency beings known as the Triadions; nasty by nature. They thrived on fear, and their basic essence was fuelled by fire energy. We cleared the transmitter and chips they had placed in Clare, and I left.

On the way home I spotted a van with the words 'Source4you' written on it. It made me smile, I felt like Abba had just sent me a text message, a great big one. I decided to ask for some clues from my oracle cards, and my Fairy Godmother showed up. I ran myself a bath and went to see Abba, who was standing chatting to my Fairy Godmother. She had a smile like an angel.

"You called Father?"

"You need to make a wish", he said.

I was not sure, I didn't want to mess up again, and I'd rather not try.

"Make your wish and on Friday night, meditate from 10pm till midnight. That way you will be detached from materialism", said Abba; Fairy Godmother smiled her great big smile, and nodded.

"Okay," I said and made my wish.

I asked Abba why my book kept being bound up by various witches. He told me that it was all past life issues, and once a month, they would damage my endeavours. I was to cut all vows, pacts, contracts and agreement with all people I suspected to be witches. There were mainly four of them. Once that was done, he asked me to lie down for my DNA program, and as usual I was encased in a test tube of energy, and light passed through me until I was transformed. 3656.

Michael took me to the retreat where I was given a silver goblet containing white light by Lady Nada. It lit me up like a million candles. I expressed my gratitude and left. Michael then took me to the Sphinx to remove any lower ego traits I was ready to shed. The Pharaoh did his stuff, and we were on our way back to the white room. Abba very kindly informed me that I had passed my test. The decision would not be reversed, so I could relax a bit. This helped a little, but I still was feeling a sense of burden. I needed to cry and release some of the stress from my body, it would help; it always did.

70. 25th Nov 2008 –
The Triadians and the Gregorians (3668)

When I was dropping my son at college, he was telling me about a dream he had. In the dream he was asked to do a job for someone, a dangerous job. At first he said no but they said he could drive a Bugatti Veyron (1000 BHP super car of his dreams), if he did it, and he said okay. Immediately I knew something was wrong; I cast my mind back to last night; I was so

160

tired when I got to bed, I couldn't remember if I placed a protective sleep pod around him or me. It was always a problem if I forgot. As I was driving home, I noticed a girl dressed in red and black (base chakra) carrying a small metal scooter (a transmitter). The next thing I spotted was' Absolute radio 'on the side of a van, and I was convinced he had been tampered with. Some of the nets I used lately were dissolving and I couldn't figure it out. Then I remembered that the Divine Director had warned me that the ET's were working on a weapon to damage my nets, and I was to rely on other resources

I went to see Abba with Michael, to discuss this latest problem. I looked amazing; my suit of armour was brilliant white, ice white, so bright I asked Abba to camouflage it, and he covered me in combat gear. Very funny. He then turned it into a nice shade of metal, just like Michael's. The transmitters and the remembrance day ET's, were two entirely separate groups. The latter, I now referred to as the Triadians. They were the ones trying to accumulate power by using lost souls, and Edinburgh Cathedral was a meeting place; one of many on our hit list. We needed to remove their power and rescue the souls. We knew we had more to do, but when and where, we weren't sure, until my dream about the house that had some kind of black portal in it. It was a residential home in the midlands, somewhere. That was all we knew, it was all we needed to know for now.

The Triadians needed the power to attack the Gregorians, their arch enemies. They intended to blow up their planet, and were too stupid to see the dire consequences of this act of war on the rest of the local universe. We had to stop them and we would, we were sure of that. Jon had been in the marines and Tess and I just had plenty of practise in these realms, and we were always careful, never over confident; it was to be treated as a secret military operation; only the three of us knew about it. Secret Angels Service (SAS for short).

We discussed what was happening with the nets, and Abba told me that they had covered the transmitters and their feet, with a sort of acid solution, which just dissolved the bottom of the nets. He told me to ask for the nets to be lined with chalcedony, which absorbs negative energy and then dissipates it. In ancient times chalices would be formed out of chalcedony and lined with silver; said to prevent poisoning.

As we spoke, Mother Earth appeared and Abba invoked the elements; all except fire as that was no good to us, it only gave them more power. We discussed a plan where Mother Earth would open a pit below the Triadions, and wind would form small tornados, spinners to force the beings in the ground, and into the pits. Jon and the rain could cover them in holy water, to weaken them, and the tornados could form one large channel, vacuuming them out and up into the light. It sounded simple enough, we all agreed, that would work. We formed a circle around Mother Earth, and cleaned one lot of ET's in a UFO, and dropped them into Abba's white rabbit hole. I needed to let their team know about the chalcedony. Before we left, I asked Abba if I should involve Jo, he said it was a lot of responsibility, but if she wanted to help it was entirely up to her.

71. 26th Nov 2008 - Bless, heal and purify

Last night, I decided to carry out a quick clearing on the plant before I went to bed. Abba helped me to remove a net full of black fog; it was related to the credit crunch. Earlier, I had noticed a newspaper at my friend's house; the headline was 'money' and it had a picture of a black light bulb with a "£" symbol on it. I realised straight away that it was a message.

I went to do my voluntary work at the hospital today and saw similar messages, "money worries", on the computer screen, and 'red' (base energy), on some business cards in the complementary therapy room. I needed to clear more energy today. The more we cleaned, the less power the Triadions, had to fuel their warfare.

When I got home, I noticed a man outside putting up a 'to let' sign on my neighbour's property. I hoped this was a sign that I would be moving. I liked my home, but my neighbours were noisy, and I needed peace and quiet. I dealt myself some oracle cards, and it was fabulous; 3 ace's (material success - a win for those entering competitions); Turkey (represented a gift (lottery) from spirit); Moose (a pat on the back for a job well done); Justice (a summing up of a situation - positive). This was the best reading I had seen in a long time. There was also a picture card of Source, so I needed to go and see Abba.

The water was a bit hotter than usual, it turned me pink as soon as I got into the bath, but it was too hot to stand. I cleared myself of any toxic energy, and Michael carried me up to the white room. I knocked on the door and we both went inside; a full house, Abba, Sananda, Thoth and even Lady Nada. I looked around and greeted everyone, and then I asked Abba what was going on.

"We have deemed you, the most worthy of the trust fund. You will win the money either this weekend or the following."

"Thank you everyone", I said. They all shook my hand and I bowed when Lady Nada took my hand.

"I should bow before you now, Janine", she said.

"Never, you will always be respected this way by me, I would not be here without your guidance, I am truly grateful."

"Now, it is time for your DNA program, please excuse us", said Abba and they all left, except Michael.

I lay down on the crystal table and the test tube surrounded me. The light passed through me, and my calibration went up to 3695. Abba informed me that I needed to ask him to bless, heal and purify me twelve times, to bring me up to 3700.

"Bless, heal and purify, bless, heal and purify, bless, heal and purify.............." Done, I hit 3701, and Michael took me to the retreat, to receive my next initiation. I sat on the throne in the centre of the room, in the main chamber, and a tube of energy surrounded me. A holographic image of a crown and another veil appeared above me; then lowered itself down, and joined within the essence of my other crown and veil. It seemed purer, if that were possible. No Divine Director, no Lady Nada. Michael brought me home. I was tired, I needed a nap.

72. 26th Nov 2008 - Mother Earth's heart

I could see more signs today saying that money was still a problem. I ran myself a hot bath, and decided to take a few oracles cards, to guide me. The grouse card came out of my medicine pack, which meant that I could choose a new super power. I was running out of ideas, I already had super speed, teleportation ability, invisibility, my swords; it was hard to think what else I needed; so, after much deliberation, I chose an extra protective shield around my physical body.

Some of these ET's really knocked me around at times. I hoped another layer of protection would help.

Michael took me to see Abba, and we decided to clear some of the negative energy from the planet, caused by money worries, greed and fear. As Mother Earth appeared in the centre of the three of us, we could see a thick black fog surrounding her. Once we removed that we could see what was influencing the negativity, apart from the media. There must have been fifteen UFOs and flying saucers, just like in the old fashioned movies, hooked into her at various points. Michael got to work cutting the chains attaching them to the planet, and Abba and I placed a large reinforced, chalcedony lined net around the whole scene; and he lifted them off and dropped them into the white rabbit hole, to be purified.

It was time for another trip into the void for me. Michael came to the back door with me, and when I opened it, there was nothing, just black, a sheer drop. Try to imagine opening your front door, and you are out there, in the universe; then remove all of the stars and planets from that image, and that's more or less it. Michael said that it was safe, and I jumped, I fell quickly at first, and then after a short while, I began to slow down. Then, I was in a cotton ball of indigo blue energy. I was in Mother Earth's heart, her beautiful lapis lazuli heart centre. I lay in the love and peace for 5 or 10 minutes; I soaked it up.

Then, the Cherubs came and gently carried me away to the large DNA strand, the double helix, to gain my new super power. They lowered me into one of the tubes, and as I floated down, I could feel an energy shield forming around me, like a crystal cloud. Fantastic, this shield dissolves negative energy on impact. The Cherubs caught me as I dropped out of the bottom of the double helix, like a new born baby, and took me back to the white room. I thanked the Cherubs and Abba, and we left.

73. 27th Nov 2008 – Selling my Soul

Last night, I dreamt my duvet cover had black patches all over it. My duvet cover is cream normally, so it was a sign that I needed to clear the energy in my room. I noticed the word 'contract' on the sides of a van in the next street, and it was playing on my mind. I called on Archangel Michael, and he told me that I needed to break a lot of vows, contracts, pacts and agreements, again. I had made one in particular, which needed my urgent attention. He said that a few years ago (about 18 or 19) I had jokingly said to some friends, whilst under the influence, that I would sell my soul to the Devil to win the lottery. I had been tricked in my sleep into signing a contract, stating that if I did win the lottery, Satan could have my soul. Oh no, he can't; I was horrified. I immediately decreed the contract null and void; Satan was fuming, as he stood and watched me ceremoniously burn the contract in the central flame.

By the time I had my bath, I was in the frame of mind to check if I had made any other stupid agreements or mistakes. I was there for a good 30 minutes burning vows, and all sorts of old contracts, and agreements relating to past lives. Mostly involving witches, religious vows, and a few with the Devil; the trickster himself saw fit to con me on more than one occasion.

I found a large clip in the back on my heart; it looked like a clock of some sort. I felt it had been placed in my astral body last night. I must remember extra protection of physical and astral bodies, when I go to sleep. Once I was cleared, we went to see Abba. I was surprised to see Lady Nada, Thoth and Sananda there, again. They had been discussing my progress.

166

I had made a couple of errors again, nothing major, and I'd been given another reprieve. Abba said he had a quest for me. He told me that there was an island in the Pacific Ocean, where a High Priest had hidden a crystal rock. This crystal had the ability to multiply energy by one million times it original power. A handy tool, but deadly in the wrong hands. Abba felt that its secret hiding place was under threat, and he wanted me to go and get the crystal, and bring it back to him (with Michael of course). He assured me, there were no traps or dangers to us at all, and we left immediately.

We travelled through a wormhole and landed on the island, in a green area of forest. There was a cave nearby, and we headed straight for it. It was a lagoon and appeared to be a dead end pretty quickly, but Michael said we needed to go into the pool, and through a cave, below sea level. It was too far to swim without oxygen. We travelled along the tunnel under water, and came out about 2 miles into the rocks.

There was an alter type area, raised up with four golden curved support arms, surrounding a sphere of light, some kind of force field. Inside the sphere was a crystal, about 2 inches across which changed shape continuously, like a cross between a rubric cube, and a Chinese puzzle, forming geometric shapes. It was fascinating and so bright.

"How can we take it out of the force field?" I asked Michael.

"Simple; program a net to the same frequency, and scoop the crystal up."

I asked for a net of the same frequency as the force field, and it encased the sphere; as the net moved upwards, it removed the crystal.

"Like taking candy from a baby", I laughed.

I gave the crystal to Michael for safe keeping, and we made our way back to the white room. As we entered the room, Michael gave the crystal to me. It felt amazing, you could feel its power; it was almost hypnotic. I passed it to Abba, and he popped it into his heart. I thanked Michael and the group for all of their support, mostly for their mercy. Even though I had been crowned a Saint, I still felt human, a mum, a woman; I still made mistakes, and I was sick of beating myself up over not being perfect enough. They were very kind to me, and I felt their love as I made my way out of the white room, and back down to Earth.

74. 28th Nov 2008 - Prince Zargon

Last night, I received another message to clear some of the negative energy from Mother Earth. Michael took me up to the white room and we sat down with Abba. The planet was infected again. We pulled three nets through, to collect the ET's; the fear related to money worries and general pollution. This was becoming a full time job for me. My client cancelled her appointment, so I did not need to go into the clinic today, as she was my only appointment. Somehow, I felt that was a bit of a test, to see if I would get sucked into the worrying about the money illusion.

I went to speak to my friend Willow; he told me I was to stay away from work for a whole week and to keep myself to myself. I had some important work coming up, and I needed to conserve my energy. It was also important for me to be creative, to counterbalance the (masculine/feminine energy on the planet. Michael said that we were needed upstairs in the white room.

When we went inside, Lady Nada, Thoth and Sananda were there, all looking quite serious.

"What have I done now?" I thought.

"Nothing", said Abba, "We have problems with war mongers in sector 14. Zargon the Warrior Prince is about to declare war on one of the nearby planets, in the same quadrant. I would like you and Michael to go and speak with him. Michael knows what to say; you are an envoy of peace, to represent me."

"When shall we leave, Father?"

"Tonight." He told us that we were not in any immediate danger, but we should still be vigilant.

About an hour later, I was looking out of my kitchen window, and I spotted a grey gutter cage on the lawn outside. I wondered what that meant, and then I realised: a cage, grass, green, heart. I closed my eyes and in my mind's eye I could see a small cage around my heart, which I promptly removed. My calibration was up to 3736.

About 6pm, I dropped my son off at his friend's for the weekend, and on the way home I noticed a large white van with an orange circle and key motif on the side. I had the feeling I was about to perform another soul retrieval on myself. I could see the number 7 over and over, and I counted three buses with 'not in service' on the front. My main channel must be blocked again. My back was aching, which was also a sign that something was wrong.

When I got home I ran a nice warm bath, lit some candles, and settled into the tub for my second clearing of the day. I began to cut ties with people and material items. If I had any chance of winning the money tonight, I needed to be unattached to everyone and everything, especially the outcome. I removed a black cap on a chain from my base and crown, which would have been what the sevens and the buses referred to: then I got to work on my heart.

I could see a shopping bag, and inside of the bag was a bottle of champagne. As I looked close, I could see a small doorway in the bottom of the bottle, and a key attached to it. I took the key and opened the little door; all of the champagne spilled out, and in the far side of the base was me, looking wet and miserable. I stepped inside and introduced myself.

"What are doing in here?" I asked.

"I'm here because nobody loves me, and the alcohol makes the pain go away" she replied.

"I love you, God loves you; you don't need anyone else, do you, really?" The wet me stood up and agreed with me. "Everybody loves you; the problem was that you didn't love yourself. I've fixed that now and I'd like you to come back into my heart, where you belong. I walked over to the new me, and one hug later she was back home in the centre of a loving heart.

"It's all white and there's a big pink chair", the wet me said.

"Relax, and get dry and warm", I said, and spotted an angel with a blanket, and a hot cup of something lovely. She'll be fine now. I could see a small bunker in my upper chest, in my higher heart, being removed. It was connected to me. I'd stopped loving myself unconditionally a long time ago. Once that was cleared, I felt a lot better.

(PM) Michael and I made our way to the white room, and were briefed by Abba. We left via the back door and travelled through the wormhole, out into the super universe. There were holes everywhere. I was amazed at how Michael found his way. We headed into another hole, which took us to a desert. There was an enormous stone Temple nearby. As we got closer to it, the guards asked us who we were: Michael said we were messengers from Source, and they let us pass.

There were three sets of gold steps, above; 1000 in all. We flew to the top, time was precious. As we approached a raised platform with a throne on it, I could see Prince Zargon; he was expecting us, by the look of it. Michael greeted him on our behalf, and informed him that Abba had sent us with an important request. He handed him a scroll.

"I know of Archangel Michael, but who is this he brings with him?" asked Zargon.

"This is Saint Serena, patron Saint of light workers", replied Michael. She is an envoy of peace, and represents Abba.

"So you are the infamous Janine of Warwick"; He stepped down from his throne and walked around me, looking me up and down as if I were a piece of expensive merchandise. Then he returned to his seat.

"Please consider the request, and accept this gift, as a sample of what you and your people could choose above war". I handed him a large emerald cut diamond, pure bliss energy. He was taken aback, as it touched his hand. I could tell that he was impressed.

"Tell Abba, I will consider his request, and give him my decision by sunset tomorrow".

"Thank you, we bid you farewell", said Michael; and we left.

As we made our way back to the white room, I apologised to Michael, saying sorry for talking, when I was asked to be silent.

"You did well, very well, he liked you. It could make all the difference to his decision", he said. Abba was pleased as well. We would have to wait and see.

(10pm) Time to meditate and keep my mind off winning the lottery - not easy. I cut all ties, and focused my attention on Source. I had cleaned so much old stuff that my calibration had gone up to 3756, and I had to go for another initiation. Michael came with me to the retreat, and once inside the main chamber, I sat on the throne, in the centre of the room. It had a star shaped energy surrounding it, which merged with my body, almost immediately. As I tried to stand up, my legs gave way, I couldn't walk. Michael caught me and carried me back to the white room. Abba told me to rest and let the energy settle in, so Michael laid me on the crystal table, and he went to sit and talk to Abba.

About 20 minutes later, I felt strong enough to walk, and sat down with them. I was told to close my eyes and relax. I began to tap my finger tips together, and all of a sudden, I was flying along the inside of a rainbow tube of light. I came out of the end and was no longer solid looking. I looked like a wire person, a grid with no matter. The world around me was the same, just lines making images; no colour or matter, more 2 dimensional than 3 dimensional. Then I fell into a black hole, and as I got to the end of the tube it was bright light, it was Source. I was Source. I lay there for at least another half an hour, keeping myself free from thought or attachment.

"3, 2, 1, time is up" said Michael, and it was 11:45pm, time for bed. Had I won, I didn't know, the jury decided at 12pm.

75. 29th Nov 2008 – To Win or not to Win?

I woke up at 5am dreaming that I was talking to some school friends, and I could see a van with 'lost forever' written on it. I spoke to Abba and was told that I had made 3 mistakes, so I had failed. I had spoken to Tess last night about my ex, nothing negative, but it was considered gossip, - a big No no; I was not to talk about people at all. I was furious. This has been going on for months.

I had put all of my energy into my growth, and I felt let down. I'm good enough to be crowned a Saint, but I have had lottery snatched from my grasp, because of a conversation that was not even negative. It was all wrong, I was heartbroken again.

76. Tie Cutting and Energy Clearing

The tie cutting and energy clearing I teach in my workshops can be used to clear your energy field, the energy in your home or work place, and so on. You can use it on friends and family, even pets and plants. It can be used at a distance, even if they are in Australia; it will still work as well as if they were in the same room.

You must get permission first, always! If not, you may suffer the consequences of your pushy uninvited actions; so I would advise you to use it wisely. All energy work must be carried out with care, and attention to detail.

I will explain how the procedure is carried out first, and then give you the information in the form of an

173

exercise, to use on yourself. I will explain distant clearing, and as you become more familiar with the exercise, you can work on distant cleansings. The more you use it on yourself, the quicker you will be able to perform the cleansing. I recommend practising it at least once a day for 21 days. At the end of the 21 days, you will know it by heart, and can use it anywhere. It comes in handy, and I even use it to clear hotel rooms when I am on holiday, or at workshops; I like to sleep in a clear space.

The first thing to do is to say a brief prayer before you start, asking God to guide and protect you and your work, to ensure that all energies that come to you, come from God. I never work without starting with a prayer; it is very important. I then invoke the Crystal Ki energies to work with me, and set my intention, meaning what you intend to happen and the goal of this exercise.

When performing an energy clearing on yourself, you can do it sitting in a chair. I work right out into my aura to level 35, which I feel is just outside of my God Self layer of my aura, which is layer 33. (It is possible to take a lift in meditation to level 33, and converse directly with God, if you so wish - I do it often). Once I have asked the energies to cut and release the negativity, I see the disc or grid of light, moving down through all of the levels in my aura, 35, 30, 25, 20, 15, 10, 5, into the crown chakra on top of my head; then slowly down through my physical body and out of the soles of my feet, and down through the aura below me, to level 35.

That way, I have cleared a sphere of my aura that is just outside of my God self layer. As a beginner, you might like to start at level 5 and come down 5, 4, 3, 2, 1, and into your body. Bring the grid slowly down through your whole body, out of your feet and down into the aura below you, 1, 2, 3, 4, 5 levels. You can think of these levels in terms of metres, if it helps your visualisation. The intention is the most important thing; the Crystal Ki energies will do the rest. As you feel more confident, you can increase the levels from 5 to 10, then 20, until you feel happy to work on 35 levels.

Once you have brought the grid through your energy field, you can then ask the Universal Crystal Ki energies of purification, to collect the debris and take it to where God wills it to be, which is either into the light, into the central flame, or back to where it came from, whichever is God's Will. If you have worked on the first 5 layers or metres, try to visualise a net ball of light forming from the lowest point, 5m below you; moving up and around the sides of the 5m radius sphere, and over the top of your aura, to 5m above you. I like to see it tied at the top so as not to let anything leak out. Your aura is now encased in a net ball of light, which will remove the debris cut free by the grid of light.

Now ask the Crystal Ki energies to remove the net and see the bottom of the ball moving up through the aura, from 5, 4, 3, 2, 1, and into your feet; then slowly up through your body and out of the top of your head. Then continue up through your aura again, from 1, 2, 3, 4, 5. At this point have a look in your mind's eye to see what is in the net, and then see it disappear into the distance as the Crystal Ki energies take it to wherever God wills it to be.

Sometimes, the net may be too heavy to lift, or have liquid in it. If this is the case, just ask for the net to be either water tight, or to be reinforced to make it stronger, and ask the energies to bring the net ball around you, then through you, and your aura, again. Never panic as the Crystal Ki energies are there to help, and all you need to do is ask for guidance, and you will receive it.

You are now clear of the rubbish, and you need to ask God and the Crystal Ki energies to fill the voids with whatever is necessary. THIS IS IMPORTANT! If you do not do this, you leave yourself wide open to be filled with more rubbish. You can do this clearing on your house if you are sitting inside of it, using the same procedure, but setting the intention to clear the house, instead of yourself.

Distant Clearing

This involves the same technique, except that you visualise the person standing about 50m away from you, and see them as transparent, in order to see the grid of light move through them, easily. See the grid moving down through their aura and through them, and out of the bottom of their feet, into the aura below them. Visualise the net ball of light forming from below them and around the sides of their aura and over the top of them, until they are also surrounded in a sphere of light. Visualise the ball moving up through their aura, their physical body, and the aura above them; and see it being taken away by the Crystal Ki energies.

Ask God and the energies to fill the voids with exactly what they need, and wait a couple of minutes for this to happen, and the clearing is complete. This procedure is very powerful and can be done on people, animals, countries and even Mother Earth, if you care to try. I regularly clear the planet using this technique, but could do with more like minds to learn the procedure, as working at this level takes a lot of energy. I find that I lose weight when I do a lot of planetary healing.

To do this distant clearing on a building, the same procedure applies. Visualise the building as a simple glass box; this box represents the building you wish to cleanse. See the grid coming down from about 10m above the roof and down through the building, through each floor, and then down into the ground, about 10m below ground level will do. Then just as you would with a person, see the net ball of light surround the building, and see it rising up from below the ground through the building and up into air, 10m. I like to look, at this point, to make sure that there is something in the net before asking the Crystal Ki energies to take it to where God wills it to be. Then ask them to fill the voids, and allow this to happen. It really is quite simple, and practise is essential if you want your home or work place to be clear.

If you have a problem seeing the net in your mind's eye, just imagine that it is happening; this is good enough, but just saying the words and not visualising it is pointless, and it will not work. It is important that you are not going to be disturbed, as once you have started the procedure; you must see it through to completion, as not doing so can be counterproductive.

Tie Cutting

Tie cutting is simple and can release us from unhealthy or controlling relationships, past traumas, and much more. I have even used it to cut ties with myself saboteur, and asking the Universe to bring in the improved version of me, visualising that new me coming all of the way into my physical body and merging with my energy. I'm sure this helped me to get motivated and to write this book.

Most of you will have heard the old saying "Tugging at my heart strings". These strings are real, albeit invisible, to the naked eye. They are negative

177

energetic psychic ties or connections. Tie cutting literally cuts you free of these connections, and freedom prevails. Not being able to move on from old lovers is the most common problem; tie cutting resolves this; but many people need to cut ties with their own family, as they can cause us a lot of distress. People can drain your life force via these connections, leaving you feeling depleted when they have gone. It is simple to cut ties with them using this visualisation technique, having first set the intention that you wish to cut the negative tie between you and whomever you choose.

1. First find a quiet place where you will not be disturbed, and set your intention to cut only the negative ties with this person or group.

2. Do the 18 breath exercise to help open your mind's eye. (Step 4 on page 180)

3. Visualise that person standing about 10m away from you, and try to get a sense of the negative connection or tie. If you cannot see one don't worry, simply imagine a black ribbon connecting you both.

4. In your mind's eye, visualise a pair of scissors cutting that ribbon, and then say these words and mean them; "I cut and release you with love and peace, I am totally free". This will release the energy you have cut free. I have seen ropes, rods, chains and other things linking people together. Depending on what needs cutting, you can visualise either, using a knife, bolt cutters for chains, or a laser for metal rods. Just visualising the tool coming in and cutting the negative tie, will do the job.

5. Ask God to fill the gaps with whatever is necessary at this time, and say thank you.

This can also be used to cut free earthbound spirits. I once had a client who had the spirit of her brother attached to her. He had died when they were children and she was now in her fifties. During the Crystal Ki chakra balancing treatment, her deceased brother told me that he wanted her to carry out a tie cutting, in order for him to pass over into the light. This is always a difficult position for me, but I did tell the lady and she was very grateful. I took her into a meditative state and let her talk to her brother and say goodbye; it was very moving for all of us. It was the right thing to do though, and the lady was pleased that he was ok, and that she had the chance to say goodbye to him. I love my work, but sometimes it can get very emotional.

Note: Negative ties made with people due to fall outs and disputes, can be reconnected if you still persist in arguing or bad mouthing the person you have cut ties with. So I advise you to cut, release, and forgive, once and for all. These connections can drain your energy and it is only yourself that you are hurting in the end.

The most important thing is to set your intention, and not to do this to anyone without their permission, although it is alright to do it to your children without theirs, as they are not old enough to make the decision for themselves. However, if you are performing this on someone, and you are unable to seek their permission, you can always ask their higher self, and the best way to do this is to ask your higher self to ask their higher self for permission, and to question if the tie cutting and energy clearing is for their highest good. If the response is anything other than a definite yes, then do not perform any tie cutting or any energy clearing, as you could be disrupting their karma, and that is not allowed. It is possible that the Universe is trying to teach them a lesson and we should keep away, and let nature take its course.

The same is true with someone's property; unless you have been given permission from the person who owns the property, you do not have any rights to do an energy clearing on it, even if you detect any negative energy in there. You are allowed to clear the building you work in, but it is important to do it when the building is as empty as possible, and set the intention that you aim to clear any negative energy only contained within the building; and not the people possibly still in there.

Space clearing on a person exercise

1. Prayer....Dear God, I ask that I am a channel of pure love and light, that all energies and information that comes to me, comes from you. I ask that this healing is for the highest good of all. Please bless and protect me as I work. Amen.

2. Affirm...I call upon the Universal Crystal Ki Healing Energies and the Energies of Purification. (3 Times)

3. Affirm....My intention is to cut and release only negative ties; to cut and release, record, memory, cause and effect, all negative psychic ties, cords, chains, implants, symbols and connections on all levels, not for the highest good of all, to be free from all those incarnate and discarnate, all negative energies, ET's or entities, to be free from individuals, parallel dimensions, groups, places, events, countries, to be free from the effects of lifetimes. To be set free, free to be.

4. Take 18 slow breaths, starting with 6 in through the nose and filling your whole body right down into the abdomen; and then breathe out through the mouth. Take 6 breaths in through the nose, filling the lungs and rib cage only, and breathe out through the mouth. Then, 6 breaths in through the nose, just filling the

upper chest this time, and out through the mouth. Then allow your breath to find its own natural rhythm. This breathing technique stimulates the pineal gland and opens the mind's eye. It also helps you to relax.

5. Affirm.... I ask the Crystal Ki Energies to cut and release all negativity as stated in my earlier intentions. If this is Gods will, so be it and so it is.

6. Close your eyes, wait a minute and visualise the cutting taking place.......Visualise a 5 metre radius grid or disc of light moving down from 5m above your head, through your aura and physical body, then out of the soles of your feet; through your aura again to 5m below you. (You may feel a little lighter after the ties have been cut.)

7. Affirm.... I ask the Crystal Ki Energies of Purification to net, release, record, memory, cause and effect, and take all negativity and debris, cut free, to be transformed and transmuted in the Central Flame, taken into the Light or be returned to where it came from, whichever is God's will.

8. Close your eyes and wait a minute, visualising the netting and releasing, taking place.
Visualise a net ball of light forming, starting 5m below you and surrounding the 5m radius sphere of your body's aura, and tied at the top. You and your aura are now surrounded in a net ball made of light. Visualise the bottom of the ball moving upwards through the bottom of your aura, then slowly through your physical body and up into the air 5m, collecting all of the rubbish that has been cut free. Have a look with your mind's eye to see what is in it. Do not worry if you cannot see anything, the tie cutting will still work. Then visualise the rubbish being taken away to where God wills it to be, as set in the intention made earlier. (You may feel the energy change after this.)

181

9. Affirm…. I ask God and the Crystal Ki Energies to please fill the voids with whatever is God's Will. **This is very important!** (Wait a minute or two while this takes place).

10. I ask my higher self to choose the protection I may need at this moment in time, and wait 10 or 20 seconds for that to settle in.

Thank God and the Crystal Ki Energies for helping you!!! Dismiss the Angels with love and peace.

NOTE: IF THE GRID OR NET BREAKS, ASK THE CRYSTAL KI ENERGIES FOR A TRIPLE LAYERED GRID & NET AND START AGAIN. It is essential that you carry out this exercise as it is written, and I advise you to use it with the utmost integrity; it is very powerful! (If you are any doubt about using it, please contact me via info@crystalki.co.uk for more information).

Check list

1. Prayer
2. Call in Angels
3. Set Intention
4. Breathing exercises
5. Ask for grid (**If it is God's will**)
6. Visualise grid moving down
7. Ask for net and for debris to be taken to wherever is God's will
8. Visualise it moving up
9. Ask Holy Spirit for gaps and voids to be filled with whatever is God's will (**This is important!**)
10. Ask higher self to surround you with protection & camouflage……Thanks God and Angels

77. Summary

Janine of Warwick, having received her Sainthood moves forward in the next set of adventures, book 4, The Avatar & the Crystal Key. In this, she attains from Saint, to Avatar and then through another 10 levels to Avatar Supreme.

In book 5, she works towards becoming a Rishi at 6000, Angel at 7000 and Archangel at 8000, surrendering her free will to God the Father.

She dedicates her life to the cause, the ascension of Mother Earth and the Shift in consciousness predicted in December 2012. She continues to work with Archangel Michael freeing the planet from invasion and the dark forces that are trying to stop the evolutionary process taking place.

The Avatar & the Crystal Key......
The next Adventure!

Note: this book has been self edited and self published, very quickly. Please try to ignore any spelling mistakes and concentrate on the messages it brings - I hope you enjoy reading it.

Peace be with you
Janine Regan-Sinclair

78. Recommended Reading

Ken Page - The Way it Works

Barbara Ann Brennan – Hands of Light

Chris Thomas – Universal Soul

Chris Thomas & Diane Baker – Everything you always wanted to know about your body but so far nobody's been able to tell you.

Deeprak Chopra – Life after Death

Gregg Braden – The Divine Matrix

Debbie Shapiro – Healing Mind, Healing Body

Sogyal Rinpoche – The Tibetan Book of Living and Dying

Diana Cooper - A Little Light on Spiritual Laws & Discover Atlantis

Chris Morton and Ceri Louise Thomas – The Mystery of the Crystal Skulls

Rhonda Byrne – The Secret

Jacqueline Memory Paterson – A Tree in Your Pocket

The Little Book of Wisdom – Dalai Lama

The Urantia Foundation – The Urantia Book

The Princess & the Pink Moon Leeches

Another fictional adaptation of many of Janine's astral adventures with Archangel Michael. This is book 3 in the Angel Warrior series of 7. It contains the all new Crystal Ki map of consciousness listing the development from Master level (950) to Oversoul level (10,000). Written as a diary, it is perfect for people with a short attention span and takes readers on an enlightening journey from Planetary Princess level (1750) to Saint Level (3500) in their spiritual development. The Crystal Ki clearing techniques are printed in the back of all of the books within the series. The attainment figures recorded are genuine and along her path she meets The Emperor of the Gods, visits The Halls of Amenti and travels to a crystal city on Jupiter, possibly our future home after 2012, who knows?

Janine Regan-Sinclair is a Crystal Ki Practitioner / Teacher and Clinical Hypnotherapist based in the United Kingdom. She developed her own healing system in 2005 called Crystal Ki Healing and The 21 day Mind Detox in 2010. She has written many magazine articles relating to the importance of self cleansing and raising consciousness. Please visit www.crystalki.co.uk for more information on treatments and training courses. Janine is also available for talks and demonstrations.

With Love
Janine x